Measurement of Construction Work

This book is to be returned on or before
the last date stamped below.

Measurement of Construction Work

Volume 1

Second Edition

Chris Wilcox FRICS, FIQS, AMBIM

and

John A. Snape ARICS, AMBIM

George Godwin Limited
The book publishing subsidiary
of the Builder Group

First published in Great Britain in 1972 by George Godwin Limited under the title *Worked Examples in Measurement of Consruction Work* Volume 1

Second edition 1980

George Godwin Limited
The book publishing subsidiary
of the Builder Group
1-3 Pemberton Row, Fleet Street
London EC4

British Library Cataloguing in Publication Data
Wilcox, Chris
    Measurement of construction work. — 2nd ed.
    Vol. 1
    1. Building — Estimates
    I. Title II. Snape, John A
    III. Worked examples in measurement of
    construction work
    624'.1   TH435

    ISBN 0-7114-5510-4

Typeset by R.S. Print & Design. Fleet Street, London
Printed and bound by Tonbridge Printers, Tonbridge, Kent

Contents

Finishings, Windows, Doors, Staircases, Joinery Fittings and Fixtures are covered in Volume 2 of this series.

List of Plates

Preface

The principal aim of the book is to demonstrate a logical and systematic approach to the measurement of construction work by the use of a wide range of worked examples appropriate to a first year course of study.

For many years examiners have complained that students do not adopt a logical sequence of measurement and cannot write adequate descriptions of the work involved. The author's own experience fully supports this contention and they have therefore placed considerable emphasis on these aspects of the work.

The text of this revised second edition has been revised to comply with the requirements of the 6th edition of the Standard Method of Measurement of Building Works. This edition of the Standard Method is accompanied by a Practice Manual and the student is recommended to make reference to this as an aid to the correct application of the rules of measurement.

The text otherwise follows closely the format of the first edition. This was intended primarily for use by quantity surveying students and by students on other advanced courses (Institute of Building, City and Guilds and others). Technician Education Council (TEC) courses, now introduced, require a knowledge of measurement at a very early stage. The authors consider the presentation of the wide range of examples, with fully detailed drawings, to be of considerable value to students at this level.

The first edition was published under the title *Worked Examples in Measurement of Construction Work.* However, both authors and publishers felt that this did not adequately reflect the full scope of the work and the title has therefore been revised.

As with the previous edition the group system of measurement is recommended and has been used in all examples. One complete chapter has been devoted to each group and each chapter opens with a description of a logical and systematic approach to the measurement of work in that group. The importance of the approach has been further emphasised by including a fully detailed approach at the commencement of each of the worked examples.

Instruction has been provided in the important technique of writing descriptions and the authors have demonstrated that the technique may be quickly acquired by the application of four simple rules. These rules have been applied to all descriptions in the worked examples and SMM phraseology has been used throughout.

In order to maintain a realistic presentation appropriate to current practice, this book has been printed in A4 size and the papers ruled in accordance with BS 3327:1970 'Specification for Stationery for Quantity Surveying'. The various schedules and drawings comply with BS 1192:1969 'Building Drawing Practice'. The drawings have been produced to recommended scales. The drawings include the constructional details so necessary to students who must now study quantities and building construction simultaneously. The dimensions have been handwritten since this is the only realistic form of presentation of this work.

The commentary which accompanies each example includes references to the appropriate SMM Rules, which have not been reproduced since it is essential that the student makes full and frequent reference to the SMM in order to obtain a thorough understanding of the Rules and their application.

The authors consider that the demonstration and discussion which takes place in the lecture room are of prime importance: but their experience proves that the learning process is considerably aided by a comprehensive text, used in conjunction with the lectures, and available to the student for detailed study and permanent reference.

Both the publishers and the authors would be interested to hear from lecturers and students who have any comments or suggestions which might contribute to further editions of this book.

CHRIS WILCOX
JOHN SNAPE

Chapter I

Introduction

The services of the quantity surveyor

The services which the quantity surveyor normally provides to his client may be summarised as follows:

(1)   Preliminary cost advice.
(2)   Cost planning.
(3)   Advice on form of contract.
(4)   Preparation of tender documents.
(5)   Advice on obtaining tenders.
(6)   Examination of tenders.
(7)   Valuation of work in progress.
(8)   Cost control.
(9)   Final account.

PRELIMINARY COST ADVICE. Even before drawings are prepared preliminary cost advice may be offered to indicate the probable cost of a proposed project, or to assess the type and size of structure which may be erected for any given expenditure. This advice is of considerable assistance to the design team and informs the client of the cost implications before any decisions are made.

COST PLANNING. The technique of cost planning makes use of cost advice during the design process. Cost planning involves a systematic analysis of the structure which enables the price for each constituent part to be valued against its performance requirements.

Several designs may then be prepared and valued so that the client may be offered a number of alternatives to satisfy his building requirements, each with its financial and design implications clearly known at the outset. Decisions on the various alternatives are made with the total budget in mind and when made establish the cost plan.

ADVICE ON FORM OF CONTRACT. Building and civil engineering projects may be carried out under various contractual conditions. The choice of the appropriate form of contract will depend on the nature of the project, the circumstances under which it is executed and the particular needs of the client.

The quantity surveyor, by reason of his wide and varied experience, is able to advise his client on the form of contract most suitable for any given project. On the whole it is advantageous to use standard forms of contract which are recognised throughout the industry. This ensures that the rights and obligations of the parties to the contract and the duties of professional advisers are clearly defined.

PREPARATION OF TENDER DOCUMENTS. The most frequently used forms of contract for constructional work are based on the use of bills of quantities as contract documents. They are accepted by all concerned as an equitable tendering basis for building and engineering contracts.

In circumstances where time is an important factor or where work must be commenced before designs are completed, bills of approximate quantities can be prepared. These incorporate the necessary financial safeguards to the client and form a satisfactory basis for valuing the work executed.

Where other forms of contract are used bills of quantities may be replaced by a specification or by schedules of prices prepared by the quantity surveyor in the form most suited to the circumstances.

ADVICE ON OBTAINING TENDERS. Tenders may be obtained either in competition or by negotiation. The most widely used procedure is to invite competitive tenders, based on bills of quantities, from selected contractors. A negotiated tender would be appropriate where the contract requires the specialised knowledge or the experience of a particular contractor or where the client may wish to employ a specified company.

A decision on the most suitable form of tender must be made at an early stage and is a subject on which the quantity surveyor can offer valuable advice.

EXAMINATION OF TENDERS. When tenders have been obtained and considered the quantity surveyor will check the appropriate tender to see that no substantial errors have been made. This ensures that the contract is not entered into on an incorrect basis which may later prove to be against the interest of both client and contractor.

Advice on obtaining tenders and examination of tenders from contractors will also apply to tenders from sub-contractors and suppliers.

VALUATION OF WORK IN PROGRESS. Under most forms of contract the contractor is paid each month for the work he has completed and for materials supplied. The quantity surveyor measures and values the work carried out and submits a recommendation for a payment on account.

COST CONTROL. During construction, variations in the work are frequently necessary, either to take account of the client's changing needs or to overcome construction problems which could not be forseen. As part of the systematic control of the cost during progress of the work, the quantity surveyor values all variations and reports their effect to keep the client and designers fully informed of the up-to-date financial position and the anticipated final cost.

FINAL ACCOUNT. The quantity surveyor is usually responsible for the calculation of the final cost of the work. This is achieved by preparing a final account in which the contract sum is adjusted to take account of all variations and other financial adjustments in accordance with the terms of the contract. The quantity surveyor negotiates with the contractor's representative to agree the final account as an equitable calculation of the final cost.

OTHER SERVICES. The quantity surveyor's services also extend to various other matters related to financial and contractual aspects of building work, such as replacement valuations for fire insurance, the settlement of fire insurance claims, the preparation of schedules of dilapidations and arbitrations arising out of disputes in building and civil engineering contracts.

The contractor's quantity surveyor

The contractor's quantity surveyor is usually responsible for preparing estimates for tender purposes and will represent the contractor when variations are measured, at valuations of work in progress and in the negotiation of final accounts, including those of sub-contractors. Other duties may include the operation of incentive schemes, ordering of materials and supplies, participation in operational planning and preparation of cost data.

Functions of the bill of quantities

The principle use of the bill of quantities in current practice is to obtain competitive tenders; for this purpose bills should be as standardised as possible in method of measurement, format and layout. Bills of quantities fully describe and accurately represent the works to be executed, including the obligations required of the contractor, and so provide a uniform basis for the preparation of competitive tenders. During the construction of a project the bills are used as a basis for financial management by the clients professional advisers and by the contractor.

Format of bills of quantities

All bills of quantities, irrespective of format, will contain some, or all, of the following items:

    (1)   Preliminaries.
    (2)   Preambles.
    (3)   Measured quantities.
    (4)   Provisional quantities.
    (5)   Prime cost and provisional sums.

In considering the bill in relation to management techniques applied by the professions and contractors it is clear that the overall efficiency in design, estimating and subsequent management could be assisted by the following forms of presentation:

TRADE ORDER BILL. Bills of this type are presented in trade sections and sub-sections in the sequence listed in the Standard Method of Measurement of Building Works, or SMM. Estimating for construction work is biased towards the trade order bill; the trade presentation is an important factor facilitating the submission of competitive tenders and developments which depart from this may be criticised on the grounds of making the tendering process more laborious. Although such bills adequately fulfil their function in obtaining competitive tenders, the full potential of the information prepared by the quantity surveyor is not realised during the management of the contract and other forms of presentation have therefore been developed.

ELEMENTAL BILL. The bill is divided into sections each of which is an important element in the building (e.g. external walls, roof, floors). The work within each section is usually billed in trade order. The elemental bill, while still forming the financial basis for the contract, is also of considerable assistance in cost planning and of value on the site since the location of most items will be apparent from their position in the bill. However, the possible advantages on the site may be outweighed by the disadvantages at the tendering stage.

SECTIONALISED TRADES BILL. This form of bill is capable of presentation either as a trade order bill or as an elemental bill. For tendering purposes presentation is in trade order, each section commencing with preamble clauses. Within each section items are grouped in elements billed in trade order sequence. The separate elements always commence at the top of a sheet so that a 'loose-leaf' form is obtained allowing the bills to be re-arranged as elemental bills for use in contract management.

OPERATIONAL BILLS. This bill divides the work into site operations as distinct from trades or elements. Materials are shown separately and labour is described in terms of the operations necessary for the construction of the building. An operation is regarded as the work done by a man or gang of men at some definite stage in the building process. The principle governing operational bills is that the description of the building work required shall follow the building process itself: both the building operations on site and the estimating, purchasing and planning in the builder's office can thus be related to the way the costs are incurred.

ACTIVITY BILLS. An activity bill is measured in accordance with the SMM and the work is billed in sections which relate to activities (or operations) established by network analysis. On site and off site activities are kept separate and manufactured goods, special suppliers and nominated specialists are billed in self-contained sections. Although this follows the general lines of the operational bill no attempt is made to separate the measurement of labour from materials.

ANNOTATED BILLS. Side notes are incorporated in the bill to indicate the location of the measured items within the building. This is of assistance to the estimator at the tender stage and to all concerned with the physical construction of the project.

Production of bills of quantities

The group system of taking off and working up, involving abstracting and billing, has been in general use for many years. In more recent years the development of more efficient systems has reduced or eliminated the working up processes. The most important techniques in current use are as follows:

GROUP SYSTEM (LONDON METHOD). This system provides the 'taker-off' with a logical system of measurement designed to promote acccurate and efficient taking off. The work is measured in a series of groups, each representing a particular section of the building without regard to the order in which items will finally appear in the bill. Since the sequence of measurement is not related to the order of the bill the working up process must involve the preparation of an abstract to collect and arrange the items in the order necessary for writing the draft bill.

The group system is most appropriate for use in examinations and has been used in the measurement of examples in the following chapters.

TRADE BY TRADE SYSTEM (NORTHERN METHOD). This involves taking off bills of quantities by trades, in order of billing, without the necessity for an abstract. Each item is taken off as a separate entity in the order in which it will eventually be billed including all relevant deductions.

CUT AND SHUFFLE SYSTEM. The group system of taking off is adopted using specially ruled dimension sheets. Each sheet is ruled into four separate slips and one item only is entered on each slip. A copy is made of each completed dimension sheet and the taker off retains the original while the copies are cut into slips, collected and sorted into bill sequence without the necessity for abstracting or billing.

COMPUTERS. There are two basic approaches to the use of computers in the preparation of bills of quantities:
- (1) To use the computer to do all calculations and sort the items into bill order, the draft bill of quantities being prepared in the normal manner by the quantity surveyor.
- (2) For the computer to do all calculations, sorting and printing of the bills on the basis of a standard library of descriptions.

One of the chief advantages of using a computer is the speed with which bills can be produced. The computer may be programmed to print out alternative forms of bill from a single set of dimensions, including, for example, a trade order bill for tendering purposes, an elemental bill for cost planning, and an activity bill for site management.

The Standard Method of Measurement

The rules governing the measurement of construction work are laid down in the Standard Method of Measurement of Building Works, authorised by agreement between the Royal Institution of Chartered Surveyors and the National Federation of Building Trades Employers. The Standard Method of Measurement provides a uniform basis for measuring building works and embodies the essentials of good practice, but more detailed information than is demanded by the document should be given where necessary in order to define the precise nature and extent of the required work. The standard method applies equally to the measurement of proposed works and of executed works.

To obtain the full rules for the measurement of any particular item the various General Rules must be taken into account. For example, to obtain the full rules for concrete in beds, first Section A applies, then Clauses F4 and F5 and finally Clause F6.8.

Practice Manual SMM 6

This manual prepared for the 6th edition, is non-mandatory and is intended to be read and used in conjunction with the Standard Method of Measurement. It has two basic purposes; first it is intended to give guidance on the communication of information relative to quantities of finished work where their value is modified by position, complexity, simplicity, repetition, eccentric distribution or other cost significant factors; second it is intended to encourage good practice in the measurement of building works.

Code for the measurement of building works in small dwellings

This code is also authorised by agreement between the Royal Institution of Chartered Surveyors and the National Federation of Building Trades Employers.

The code provides a uniform basis for measuring building works in small dwellings (houses, bungalows, flats and maisonettes); its use is restricted to buildings not exceeding two storeys in height and each dwelling not exceeding 111.48 square metres floor area. It embodies the essentials of good practice but more detailed information than is demanded by the document should be given where necessary in order to define the precise nature and extent of the required work. The code applies equally to the measurement of proposed works and of executed works.

Chapter II

Principles of measurement and description

Dimension paper

The size and ruling of dimension paper are given in BS 3327 : 1970 'Specification for Stationery for Quantity Surveying'. The specified size is A4 in the series of international paper sizes, 210 mm horizontal and 297 mm vertical. The rulings, widths and purpose of columns on the face and reverse sides of dimension paper illustrated in Figure 1 and Figure 2.

mm	14 mm	15 mm	16 mm	55 mm	14 mm	15 mm	16 mm	56 mm
BINDING MARGIN	TIMESING	DIMENSIONS	SQUARING	DESCRIPTIONS	TIMESING	DIMENSIONS	SQUARING	DESCRIPTIONS

Figure 1 DIMENSION PAPER (FACE SIDE)

mm	15 mm	16 mm	55 mm	14 mm	15 mm	16 mm	54 mm	9 mm
TIMESING	DIMENSIONS	SQUARING	DESCRIPTIONS	TIMESING	DIMENSIONS	SQUARING	DESCRIPTIONS	BINDING MARGIN

Figure 2 DIMENSION PAPER (REVERSE SIDE)

Setting out and order of dimensions

The measurement items are set down under each other on the dimension sheets and are spaced well apart to ensure clarity. Adequate spacing also enables the taker off to insert in the appropriate place any items which may have been overlooked. Neatness and good handwriting are also essential factors of presentation.

ORDER OF DIMENSIONS. The order of stating dimensions in descriptions shall be consistent and generally in the sequence of length, width and height (SMM A4). Good practice demands that this sequence is also adopted when entering measurements in the dimension columns as in Figure 3.

12.00 8.60 1.50						A cubic measurement 12.00 m long 8.60 m wide 1.50 m high (or deep)
12.00 8.60						A square measurement 12.00 m long 8.60 m wide height (or depth) stated in description
12.00						A linear measurement 12.00 m long width & height (or depth) stated in description
6						An enumerated item 6 No length, width & height (or depth) stated in description

Figure 3

TIMESING. Some items may occur several times during taking off and in order to avoid re-writing the items the appropriate measurements may be multiplied or 'timesed'. The timesing figure is written in the timesing column and separated from the measurement by a diagonal stroke. Any item previously timesed may be timesed again, each timesing multiplying everything to the right of the diagonal stroke.

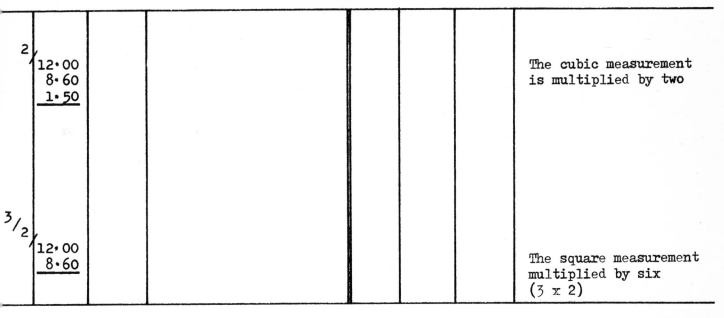

Figure 4

DOTTING ON. Timesing a previously timesed measurement is not always practicable but where additional items occur the timesing factor may be increased by 'dotting on' (adding) the additional values.

Figure 5

BRACKETS. A bracket is used whenever more than one measurement relates to a description or group of descriptions. The total quantity indicated by the measurements within the bracket is set against each related description on the abstract.

12·00 8·60	103·20							
10·50 6·00	63·00							
11·50 7·00	80·50						Total quantity to be abstracted	
	246·70							

Figure 6

ALTERATIONS IN DIMENSIONS. Dimensions should never be erased or altered. Incorrect dimensions should be cancelled by writing NIL in the squaring column alongside the incorrect figures and the extent of the cancellation indicated by brackets or arrow heads. The correct dimensions may then be written clearly in the dimension column.

12·00 8·00	NIL							
12·00 8·60								
10·50 6·00	NIL							
11·50 7·00								
10·50 6·50								
11·00 7·00								

Figure 7

WASTE CALCULATIONS. The preliminary (waste) calculations involved in determining the dimensions and any related explanatory comments should be written clearly on the right hand side of the description column. The risk of error will then be reduced since these calculations may be checked during working up and in addition the process by which the dimensions were determined will be made clear for later reference.

Waste calculations are written to three decimal places and the results reduced to the nearest 10 mm (SMM A3) before transfer to the dimension column.

Writing descriptions

The first essential of a description in a bill of quantities is that it should satisfy the requirements laid down in the SMM and in principle any description which fails to do so is incorrect. The various clauses in the SMM indicate the essentials of the description but more information should be given where necessary in order to define the precise nature and extent of the work. SMM A4 indicates that certain items are 'deemed to be included' and therefore no reference is made to these items in any description. The practical application of the SMM must be combined with a detailed knowledge of construction technology in order to formulate clear and concise descriptions.

A standard mode of describing items or means of expression is required and in practice the use of standard phraseology, such as that developed by Leonard Fletcher and Thomas Moore, is recommended. However, in most circumstances and in particular during examinations, the student does not have the assistance of such documents; he is therefore advised to use the phraseology of the SMM since under these conditions this is his only available reference.

The technique of writing descriptions may be quickly acquired by the careful application of four simple rules:

(1)   List the essentials laid down in relevant SMM clauses.
(2)   Use SMM phraseology.
(3)   Select necessary information from drawings and specification.
(4)   Re-arrange the sequence, if necessary, to provide a clear and concise description.

The observance of these four rules will avoid the necessity for committing to memory any descriptions whatsoever and should enable the student to describe any items of work within the scope of the SMM.

This technique is best illustrated by examples on pages 10, and 11.

Standard Phraseology for Bills of Quantities

STANDARD PHRASEOLOGY, developed by Leonard Fletcher and Thomas Moore, employs a systematic presentation of words and phrases which enables the build-up of standardised work item descriptions for bills of quantities. In addition, the system's process of progression through various levels of words and phrases automatically establishes the correct order for any selection of items.

The use of STANDARD PHRASEOLOGY leads to improved communication due to the consistency of description, it being clearly advantageous to have the same work always described in the same terms, regardless of the building type, geographical location, client, architect or quantity surveyor involved.

The use of both STANDARD PHRASEOLOGY and a standard sequence of presentation in descriptions is now more important than ever with the increasing use of computers for the production of bills of quantities.

Preliminaries

The preliminaries bill describes the nature and extent of the work, the type of contract and all factors affecting the physical execution of the works. Most preliminary items are contained in Section B of the SMM, but any additional obligations or restrictions imposed on the contractor by the employer must be added by the surveyor. The standardisation working party of the RICS has produced a 'Specimen example of a bill of standard preliminaries' based on the RIBA standard form of contract and this can be used for reference.

Example 1. Length of straight trench for 100 mm drain starting ground level average 0.85 m deep.

SMM W1 nature of ground	USUALLY REFERRED TO IN PREAMBLES
SMM W3 Excavating pipe trenches shall be given in metres stating	

(1)	STARTING LEVEL	GROUND LEVEL
(2)	DEPTH RANGE IN INCREMENTS OF 2·00 m	MAXIMUM DEPTH NOT EXCEEDING 2·00 m
(3)	AVERAGE DEPTH TO NEAREST 0·25 m	AVERAGE DEPTH 0·75 m
(4)	CURVED IF APPROPRIATE	NOT APPROPRIATE
(5)	NOMINAL SIZE OF PIPE (TRENCHES TO RECEIVE PIPES NOT EXCEEDING 200 mm NOMINAL SIZE MAY BE GROUPED TOGETHER AND SO DESCRIBED)	PIPES NOT EXCEEDING 200 mm NORMAL SIZE
(6)	EARTHWORK SUPPORT, TREATING BOTTOMS, FILLING IN, COMPACTION AND DISPOSAL OF SURPLUS SOIL SHALL BE GIVEN IN THE DESCRIPTIONS	INCLUDING EARTHWORK SUPPORT, GRADING BOTTOMS, FILLING IN, COMPACTION AND REMOVAL OF SURPLUS SPOIL FROM SITE

Figure 8

Completed description: Excavating pipe trench starting ground level maximum depth not exceeding 2.00 m average depth 0.75 m for pipe not exceeding 200 mm nominal size including earthwork support, grading bottoms, filling in, compaction and removal of surplus spoil from site.

Note (1) SMM phraseology as rule 2 (page 9).
(2) No re-arrangement of sequence required under rule 4 (page 9).

Example 2.   100 mm wide hessian base bituminous felt d.p.c. to block partition

SMM G37	
(1) KIND AND QUALITY OF DAMP PROOF MATERIAL	HESSIAN BASE BITUMINOUS FELT
(2) GAUGE, THICKNESS OR SUBSTANCE	$3 \cdot 8 \text{ kg/m}^2$
(3) NUMBER OF LAYERS	ONE
(4) COMPOSITION AND MIX OF BEDDING MATERIALS	GAUGED LIME MORTAR (1:1:6)
(5) DAMP-PROOF COURSES NOT EXCEEDING 225 mm WIDE GIVEN IN METRES STATING THE WIDTH	100 mm WIDE
(6) NO ALLOWANCE FOR LAPS STATED IN DESCRIPTION	NO ALLOWANCE FOR LAPS
(7) HORIZONTAL, RAKING, VERTICAL, CURVED, EACH SO DESCRIBED	HORIZONTAL
(8) CUTTING TO CURVE DESCRIBED IF NECESSARY	NOT NECESSARY
(9) POINTING EXPOSED EDGE	DEEMED TO BE INCLUDED

Figure 9

Completed description: One layer hessian based bituminous felt horizontal damp proof course weighing 3.8 kg/m² 100 mm wide bedded in gauged lime mortar (1:1:6) no allowance made for laps.

Note   (1)   SMM phraseology as rule 2 (page 9).
       (2)   Sequence rearranged under rule 4 (page 9).

REPEAT DIMENSIONS. Where two or more descriptions relate to one group of dimensions repetition of the dimensions is avoided by using ampersand (&) written in the description column to clearly separate the descriptions.

Preambles

It is not usual to provide a separate specification when bills of quantities form part of the contract and hence it is necessary to specify the quality of materials and the standard of workmanship required. This information is conveyed to the contractor by means of preamble clauses inserted in each work section of the bill. The principal advantage of this procedure is that the billed descriptions are more concise since repetition of the information listed in the preambles is avoided.

Preambles, like preliminaries, are not usually written during taking off but are inserted in the bill during the working up process. Trade preambles are grouped together at the commencement of each work section and should be produced on a separate page to facilitate circulation to sub-contractors and suppliers.

Provisional and prime cost sums

Where provisional and prime cost sums are included in bills of quantities the choice of terms shall be made in conformity with the following definitions unless otherwise provided in the conditions of contract. (SMM A8.)

    (i)   The term 'provisional sum' is defined as a sum provided for work or for costs which cannot be entirely foreseen, defined or detailed at the time the tendering documents are issued.

    (ii)   The term 'prime cost sum' is defined as a sum provided for work or services to be executed by a nominated sub-contractor, a statutory authority, or a public under-taking or for materials or goods to be obtained from a nominated supplier. Such sum shall be deemed to be exclusive of any profit required by the general contractor and provision shall be made for the addition thereof.

Reference must also be made to SMM B 9 for works by nominated sub-contractors, to SMM B10 for goods and materials from nominated suppliers and to SMM B11 for works by public bodies.

Example 1.   Provisional sum £120 for connection to sewer and making good highway (SMM B11 W8).

Include the provisional sum of £120 (one hundred and twenty pounds) for connecting end of drain to public highway to be carried out by the local Authority.	Item				

Figure 10

Example 2.   Prime cost sum £800 for patent partitions by nominated sub-contractor (SMM B29)

Include the prime cost sum of £800 (eight hundred pounds) for patent partitions to be executed by nominated sub-contractor.	Item				
Add for profit	%				
General attendance	Item				

Figure 11

Example 3. Prime cost sum £55 for ironmongery to doors and windows by nominated supplier (SMM B10 and N32).

Include the prime cost sum of £55 (fifty-five pounds) for ironmongery to be supplied by a nominated supplier. Add for profit	Item %			

Figure 12.

Provisional and prime cost sums are best presented in a separate bill but if spread throughout the bill of quantities a separate list summarising all such items should be inserted at the end of the bill.

General approach to taking off (Group system)

Taking off is a very practical technique which involves four principle factors:

(1) A methodical and consistent approach.
(2) A sound knowledge of construction technology in order to interpret the drawings.
(3) Application of the rules of measurement laid down in the SMM.
(4) Sufficient knowledge of mensuration to calculate the measurements.

A methodical and consistent approach to the measurement of construction work is the key to efficent taking off. The first step in this approach is to divide the project into units of manageable proportions. For example, a project might involve several buildings on a common site, in which case each building would be treated as a separate unit.

The second step involves the measurement of the work in each unit in a series of groups, each representing a particular section of the building. The logical sequence of measurement follows closely the order of construction and the groups involved in buildings of traditional construction are:

Structural groups

(a) Foundations and work up to damp proof course
(b) Walls, partitions and external finishings
(c) Fires and vents
(d) Roofs
(e) Floors

Finishing groups

(f) Internal finishings
(g) Windows
(h) Doors
(i) Staircases
(j) Fittings and fixtures

Service groups

(k) Plumbing and engineering installations
(l) Electrical installation
(m) Drainage
(n) External works

Modification of these groups is inevitably required for buildings of non-traditional construction or for works involving demolition and alterations. In these circumstances the sequence of measurement can be determined only after careful consideration of each individual project.

One of the basic principles of taking off from drawings is to measure over all openings, recesses, projections and similar features which can be more easily dealt with by separate adjustment. For example, walls and finishings are measured over all openings and adjustments subsequently made during the measurement of the window and door groups, since at this stage the taker off will have full knowledge of the actual size of the windows and doors and hence the size of relevant openings.

DEDUCTIONS. The principle of measuring overall inevitably results in deductions being made to previously measured quantities. Such deductions are measured under the normal rules but the description is preceded by the abreviation 'ddt'. In order to avoid confusion the description immediately following a deduction may be marked 'add'.

HEADINGS. Headings are essential in taking off in order that the dimension sheets may be identified with a particular contract and also to indicate the sequence of measurement for later reference.

The title of the contract must appear at the head of each dimension sheet and is usually written on the first sheet but rubber-stamped on all subsequent sheets. In large contracts where several buildings are involved the name of the building unit should be incorporated in the title on the appropriate dimension sheets.

The work in each unit is measured in a series of groups and each group must be identified by commencing with the appropriate heading.

The sequence of measurement within each group is indicated by suitable sign-posts (side notes) written in the description column and enclosed by brackets.

Appropriate headings are also required by the SMM where a group of items are to be billed together, e.g. concrete work (SMM F3).

COLUMN NUMBERING. Each column of dimensions must be identified by numbering in sequence. This is useful for reference purposes and provides a check which ensures that the dimensions are complete.

EXTRA OVER. The SMM requires that certain items of work are measured as 'Extra over' and not as full value. This means that the estimator must allow only for the extra cost of the item over and above the value of previously measured work.

e.g. (1) SMM G14   Brick facework shall be given as extra over the brickwork on which it occurs.

(2) SMM R10   Pipe fittings shall each be enumerated separately as extra over the pipes in which they occur.

ABBREVIATIONS. A saving in space and time involved in taking off is made by the use of abbreviations when writing descriptions. There are no fully accepted standard abbreviations and the taker off may use any abbreviations whatsoever provided that the meaning is clear and unambiguous. BS 1192 : 1969 'Building Drawing Practice' incorporates a list of recommended abbreviations for components and materials for use on drawings which are also suitable for use when taking off. In practice this list is considerably extended by the shortening of familiar words in the descriptions. A list of abbreviations in common use is set out in Appendix A.

DRAWN INFORMATION (SMM A5). The majority of work sections in the SMM refer to drawn information. It is intended that this drawn information should normally exist at measurement stage. Three types of drawing are referred to:—

(a) Location drawings, required in the majority of work sections.
(b) Component details, working drawings required mainly in the composite items section of woodwork.
(c) Bill diagrams, which can be used throughout the rules as an adjunct to brief descriptions.

The requirement to give a general description of the work where stipulated, will be deemed to be satisfied where adequate location drawings are provided.

PLANT. The SMM requires the inclusion of an item for bringing to site and removing from site and an item for maintaining on site all plant required for most trade sections. No reference to these items is made during taking off as these are later incorporated by the worker up.

PROTECTION ITEMS. The SMM requires the inclusion of protection items at the end of most trade sections. No reference to these items is made during taking off as these are later incorporated by the worker up.

SCHEDULES. Scheduling is a method of communicating design decisions. The schedules should be confined to subjects which are numerous and repetitive and are more easily described by words than drawings. A schedule usually contains two categories of information. (1) A specification of materials, components or activities. (2) The location of these specifications. Typical subjects for schedules include windows, doors, ironmongery, finishings, steel reinforcement and manholes.

Specimen schedules are illustrated in BS 1192 : 1969 'Building Drawing Practice'.

Schedules provide the essential information in a concise, tabulated form for easy reference as a more practical alternative to embodying the details throughout the drawings. This saves time involved in searching for information and where schedules are not provided by the architect the taker off is well advised to prepare his own.

INSTRUCTIONS TO WORKER UP. It is often necessary for the taker off to convey to the worker up instructions relating to the processing of the dimensions. This is done by writing a note across the dimension sheet under the heading 'Worker up' to isolate the instruction from adjoining descriptions.

QUERY SHEETS. During the course of taking off the quantity surveyor invariably encounters problems involving interpretation of the drawings which require a decision from the architect. A list of the queries is prepared in triplicate and two copies submitted to the architect in order that he may append his answer, sign the sheets and return one copy to the quantity surveyor.

PROVISIONAL QUANTITIES. Bills of quantities shall fully describe and accurately represent the quantity and quality of the works to be carried out. Work which cannot be measured shall be given as a provisional sum. Work the extent of which is not known shall be described as provisional or given in a bill of approximate quantities (SMM A2). Where provisional quantities are required they are measured as accurately as possible under the normal rules but are marked PROVISIONAL and the quantity adjusted when the extent of the work becomes known.

DIMENSIONS FOR TIMBER. All sizes are deemed to be basic (nominal) sizes unless stated as finished sizes (SMM N12). Planing margins must be stated in the bill of quantities and should either be specific to the works or refer to a standard specification such as BS 4471 : 1969 Dimensions for Softwood?

Chapter III

Simple Foundations

Approach

(1) Where a large project includes several buildings measure each as a separate unit.

(2) Examine the drawings for each unit and check that the overall external dimensions equal the sum of the internal dimensions, including the thickness of walls or floors.

(3) The taker off must apply his knowledge of construcion technology to determine the sequence of construction for each foundation, which in most cases will provide a logical sequence of measurement.

(4) Each foundation must be considered on its merits but a typical sequence of measurement would be:

> Site preparation
> Surface excavation and disposal of excavated material
> Trench excavation and disposal of excavated material—strip foundations
> Earthwork support
> Treatment to bottom of excavation
> Concrete strip or raft foundation and adjustment of disposal
> Brickwork and adjustment of disposal
> Damp-proof course
> Facework
> Surface reinstatement
> Hardcore filling
> Concrete bed
> Damp-proof membrane
> Disposal of water

Measurement of foundations

SITE PREPARATION. The quantity surveyor must make a detailed study of the drawings in order to become familiar with the project before visiting the site to ascertain the nature and extent of the site preparation required. During the site visit he should record details of any turf, paved areas or vegetable soil and the size and location of any trees, hedges, bushes, etc., which may have to be removed (SMM D5—D9).

SURFACE EXCAVATION. Excavating topsoil which is required to be preserved is measured in square metres irrespective of depth (SMM D9). Where topsoil is not to be preserved or where there is no topsoil, excavation is measured in cubic metres as excavating to reduce level (SMM D13).

After the removal of topsoil any further excavation necessary to reduce the site level is measured over the building area, to the outside of the projecting foundation, as reduced level excavation (SMM D13). Such surface excavation should be measured before the foundation trenches, pits, etc., since this is the more economical method.

The depth of surface excavation is calculated by comparing the ground levels shown on the drawings with the reduced level required. In the case of simple buildings levels may be shown only at the corners of the building, in which case a straightforward average of the levels will suffice only where the whole site area is to be excavated or where the whole site area is to be filled.

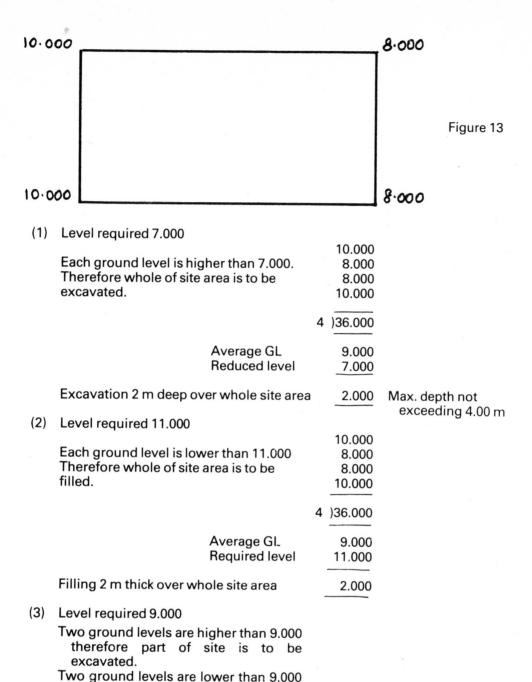

10.000   8.000

Figure 13

10.000   8.000

(1) Level required 7.000

		10.000
Each ground level is higher than 7.000.		8.000
Therefore whole of site area is to be		8.000
excavated.		10.000
	4)36.000	
Average GL		9.000
Reduced level		7.000
Excavation 2 m deep over whole site area		2.000

Max. depth not exceeding 4.00 m

(2) Level required 11.000

		10.000
Each ground level is lower than 11.000		8.000
Therefore whole of site area is to be		8.000
filled.		10.000
	4)36.000	
Average GL		9.000
Required level		11.000
Filling 2 m thick over whole site area		2.000

(3) Level required 9.000

Two ground levels are higher than 9.000 therefore part of site is to be excavated.

Two ground levels are lower than 9.000 therefore remainder of site is to be filled.

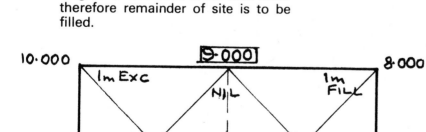

10·000   9·000   8·000

1m Exc   1m FILL

NIL

EXCAVATION   FILLING.

NIL

1m Exc   1m FILL

10·000   9·000   8·000

Figure 14

An average of the ground levels in this case indicates that neither excavation nor filling is required, which is obviously incorrect.	10.000
	8.000
	8.000
	10.000

Average GL	9.000
Required level	9.000
	NIL

The taker off must therefore consider each ground level independently to determine the depth of excavation or filling at each appropriate point.

For larger or more complex buildings more detailed information is usually provided and often includes a grid of ground levels which enables the taker off to measure the surface excavation with a greater degree of accuracy.

The grid divides the site area into a series of identical squares and the ground levels are recorded at the corners of each square. Subsequent calculations assume that the ground slopes evenly between levels so that a small grid module produces a greater degree of accuracy than a larger module. In practice a 3 metre to 10 metre grid should prove adequate for general building purposes.

The use of a grid enables the taker off to calculate the average ground level for each square. Since the squares are of identical size these levels in turn may be averaged to give an average level appropriate to the whole site area.

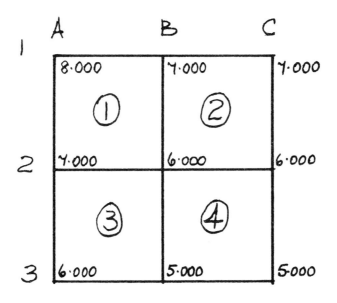

Figure 15

Average Level Grid 1	**Average Level Grid 2**
8.000	7.000
7.000	7.000
6.000	6.000
7.000	6.000
4)28.000	4)26.000
7.000	6.500

Average Level Grid 3

```
        7.000
        6.000
        5.000
        6.000
        _____
4  )24.000
        _____

        6.000
        _____
```

Average Level Grid 4

```
        6.000
        6.000
        5.000
        5.000
        _____
4  )22.000
        _____

        5.500
        _____
```

Average Level whole site area

Average Level Grid 1				7.000
"	"	"	2	6.500
"	"	"	3	6.000
"	"	"	4	5.500

```
        4 )25.000
            _____

            6.250
            _____
```

A careful study of this example shows that level B2 is included in the calculation for each of the four grid squares while, for example, level B1 appears in grid squares 1 and 2 and level A1 in square 1 only. The previous calculation may therefore be simplified by multiplying the level at each grid point by the number of squares intersecting at that point and dividing the total by four times the number of squares in the grid.

Grid point	A1	8.000	x	1	=	8.000
	B1	7.000	x	2	=	14.000
	C1	7.000	x	1	=	7.000
	A2	7.000	x	2	=	14.000
	B2	6.000	x	4	=	24.000
	C2	6.000	x	2	=	12.000
	A3	6.000	x	1	=	6.000
	B3	5.000	x	2	=	10.000
	C3	5.000	x	1	=	5.000

```
4 grid squares x 4   =              16 )100.000
                                        _____

                                         6.250
                                        _____
```

This method of calculation, which includes the ground level at each corner of each grid square, is more accurate than merely averaging the nine levels on the grid which would produce an average level of 6.333.

CUT AND FILL LINE. After removal of topsoil further surface excavation may be required over part of the site area and filling required over the remainder. The ground levels on the drawing may then be used to calculate the position of a 'cut and fill line' indicating the level at which no further excavation will be required. The area on the high side of the cut and fill line will require further excavation to reduce levels and the area on the low side filling to make up levels.

Example.

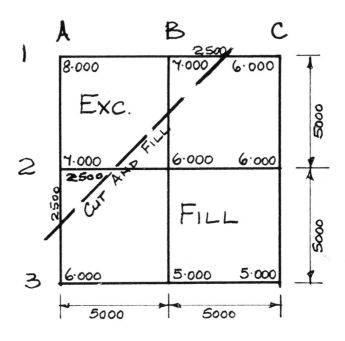

Figure 16

Plot level 6.500 for 'cut and fill'

Consider line 1. Level 6.500 lies between grid points B1 and C1.

B1 - C1 500   fall 7.000 − 6.000 = 1.000
          1000   B1 7.000 − 6.500 = 0.500

$$\frac{500}{1000} \times 5000 = \textbf{2500 from point B1}$$

Consider line 2. Level 6.500 lies between grid points A2 and B2.

A2 - B2 500   fall 7.000 − 6.000 = 1.000
          1000   A2 7.000 − 6.500 = 0.500

$$\frac{500}{1000} \times 5000 = \textbf{2500 from point A2}$$

Consider line 3. Level 6.500 does not occur.

Consider line A. Level 6.500 lies between grid points A2 and A3.

A2 - A3 500   fall 7.000 − 6.000 = 1.000
          1000   A2 7.000 − 6.500 = 0.500

$$\frac{500}{1000} \times 5000 = \textbf{2500 from point A2}$$

TRENCH EXCAVATION. The most accurate method of measuring foundation trenches is to measure each length of trench separately, considering its width and depth. For simple foundations it is sufficiently accurate to calculate an average depth of trench appropriate to the whole foundation. Where the foundations are of uniform width the taker off should collect in the waste the lengths of all trenches to calculate the total length. Should the foundation include trenches of different widths each width must be collected separately, as is usually required in the case of trenches for external walls and internal walls.

Trenches to receive foundations are usually the same width as the concrete foundation. In more complex foundations working space may be required and excavation and filling must be measured as a single item for each type of excavation (SMM D12). Trenches not exceeding 0.30 m wide are measured in metres stating the avarage depth to the nearest 0.25 m. Trenches over 0.30 m wide are measured in cubic metres (SMM D13).

Example.

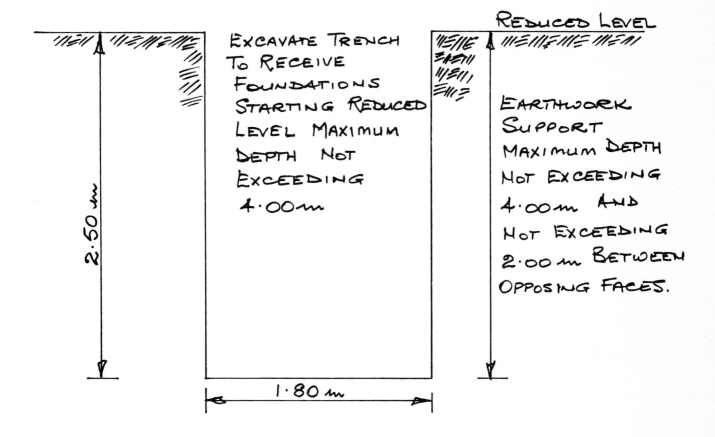

Figure 17

On sloping sites where the foundation is stepped the minimum depth of excavation is measured for the full length of trench. The additional depth of excavation between steps is then measured separately, changing the depth classification where necessary (SMM D11).

EARTHWORK SUPPORT. The term implies the use of timbers or other materials to support the sides of excavation, when in fact no such support may be involved. The measured item indicates only the area of excavation which may require support with the appropriate classification and must be measured whether or not any is in fact required (SMM D15). The contractor will decide the nature and extent of the support, if any, and will price the item accordingly. This decision involves a degree of risk since the contractor is responsible for upholding the sides of excavation and failure to provide adequate support may result in the additional expense of any re-excavation.

Earthwork support must be measured to the full depth of any excavation which is over 0.25 m deep (SMM D15).

CONCRETE IN FOUNDATIONS. Concrete strip foundations should be measured the full length of the trench, ignoring steps, and any additional concrete and formwork at steps measured later. The extra thickness of concrete at a step may involve a change in description to comply with the stages in SMM F5.

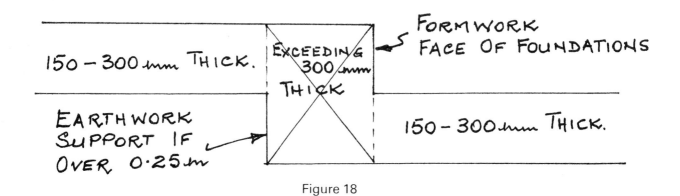

Figure 18

In practice this change of stage is often ignored, in which case the whole of the concrete in Figure 18 would be measured and described as '150 - 300 mm thick'.

BRICKWORK. The size of bricks recommended in BS 3921 Part 2: 1969 is 215 x 102.5 x 65 mm which with a 10 mm mortar joint produces a standard format (bricks) of 225 x 112.5 x 75 mm. The practice of designating wall thicknesses and length, including the widths in piers, by the format size, e.g. 112.5 mm for half brick walls and so on, is recommended and has been adopted throughout the text.

Brickwork in this group shall be classified as FOUNDATIONS and given under an appropriate heading (SMM G3).

WALL GIRTHS. Brickwork and blockwork are measured the mean length by the average height (SMM G4), the mean length being measured along the centre-line of the wall and calculated from the dimensions shown on the drawing.

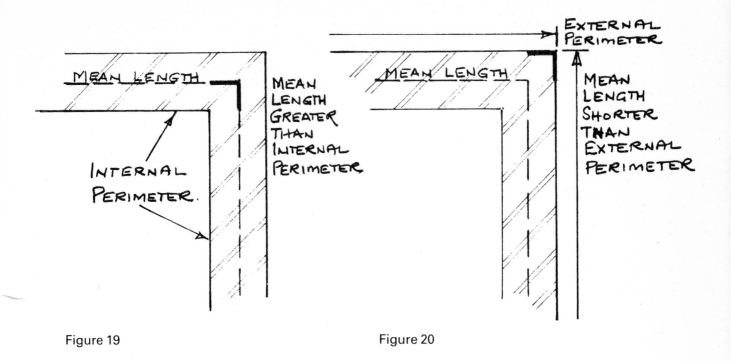

Figure 19   Figure 20

At each external angle the mean length of the wall exceeds the internal perimeter and falls short of the external perimeter by a length equal to the thickness of the wall. The reverse applies in the case of each internal angle.

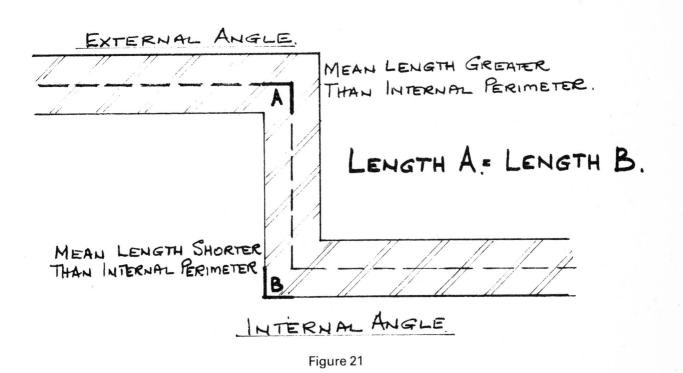

Figure 21

It is clear that an external angle **cancels** an internal angle. The mean length is calculated by adding to the external perimeter or deducting from the internal perimeter one one wall thickness for each external angle in excess of the number of internal angles.

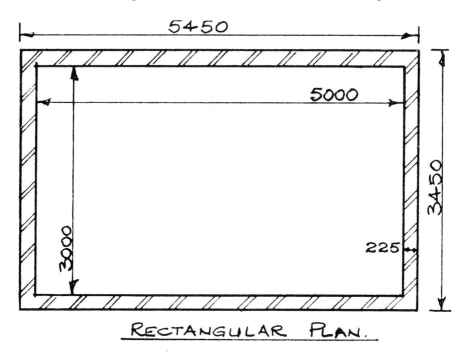

RECTANGULAR PLAN.

Figure 22

Method A—use internal dimensions

length		5.000
width		3.000
	2/	
		8.000
Internal perimeter		16.000
Add external angles	4/	
	0.225	0.900
Mean length		16.900

Method B—use external dimensions

length		5.450
width		3.450
	2/	
		8.900
External perimeter		17.800
Ddt. external angles	4/	
	0.225	0.900
Mean length		16.900

Method C—use a combination of internal and
external dimensions to in-
clude the wall thicknesses
at angles.

length	5.450
width	3.000
	2/
	8.450
Mean length	16.900

These calculations may be checked by adding together the lengths of each portion of wall:—

	5.450
	3.000
	5.450
	3.000
Mean length	16.900

This method must be used where the wall plan includes irregular angles.

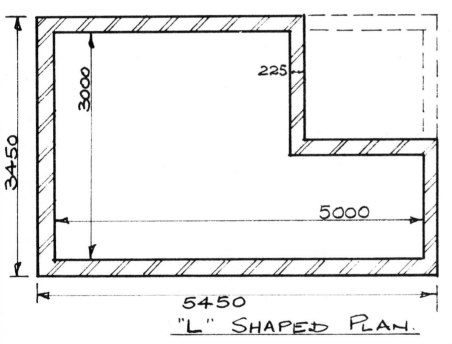

225

3000

3450

5000

5450

"L" SHAPED PLAN.

EXTERNAL ANGLES 5
INTERNAL ANGLES 1
EXCESS 4

MEAN LENGTH OF
WALLS EXACTLY
AS RECTANGULAR
PLAN.

Figure 23

Method A

length		5.000
width		3.000
		2/
		8.000
Internal perimeter		16.000
Add external angles	4/	
	0.225	0.900
Mean length		16.900

Method B	length		5.450
	width		3.450
		2/	8.900
	External perimeter		17.800
	Ddt. external angles	4/ 0.225	0.900
	Mean length		16.900
Method C	length		5.450
	width		3.000
		2/	8.900
	Mean length		17.800

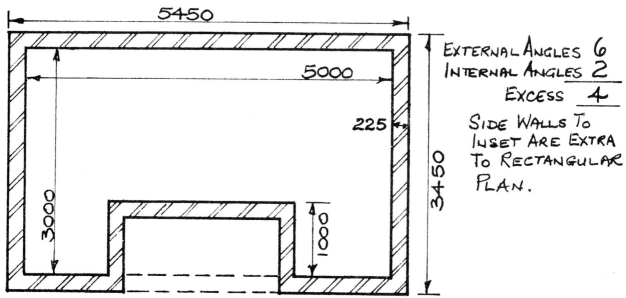

5450

5000

225

3450

3000

1000

EXTERNAL ANGLES 6
INTERNAL ANGLES 2
EXCESS 4

SIDE WALLS TO
INSET ARE EXTRA
TO RECTANGULAR
PLAN.

PLAN WITH INSET.

Figure 24

Method A	length		5.000
	width		3.000
		2/	8.000
			16.000
	insets 2/	1.000	2.000
	Internal perimeter		18.000
	Add external angles	4/ 0.225	0.900
	Mean length		18.900

Method B

length			5.450
width			3.450
			2/ 8.900
Insets 2/ 1.000			17.800
			2.000
External perimeter			19.800
Ddt. external angles	4/	0.225	0.900
Mean length			18.900

Method C

length	5.450
width	3.000
insets	1.000
	2/ 9.450
Mean length	18.900

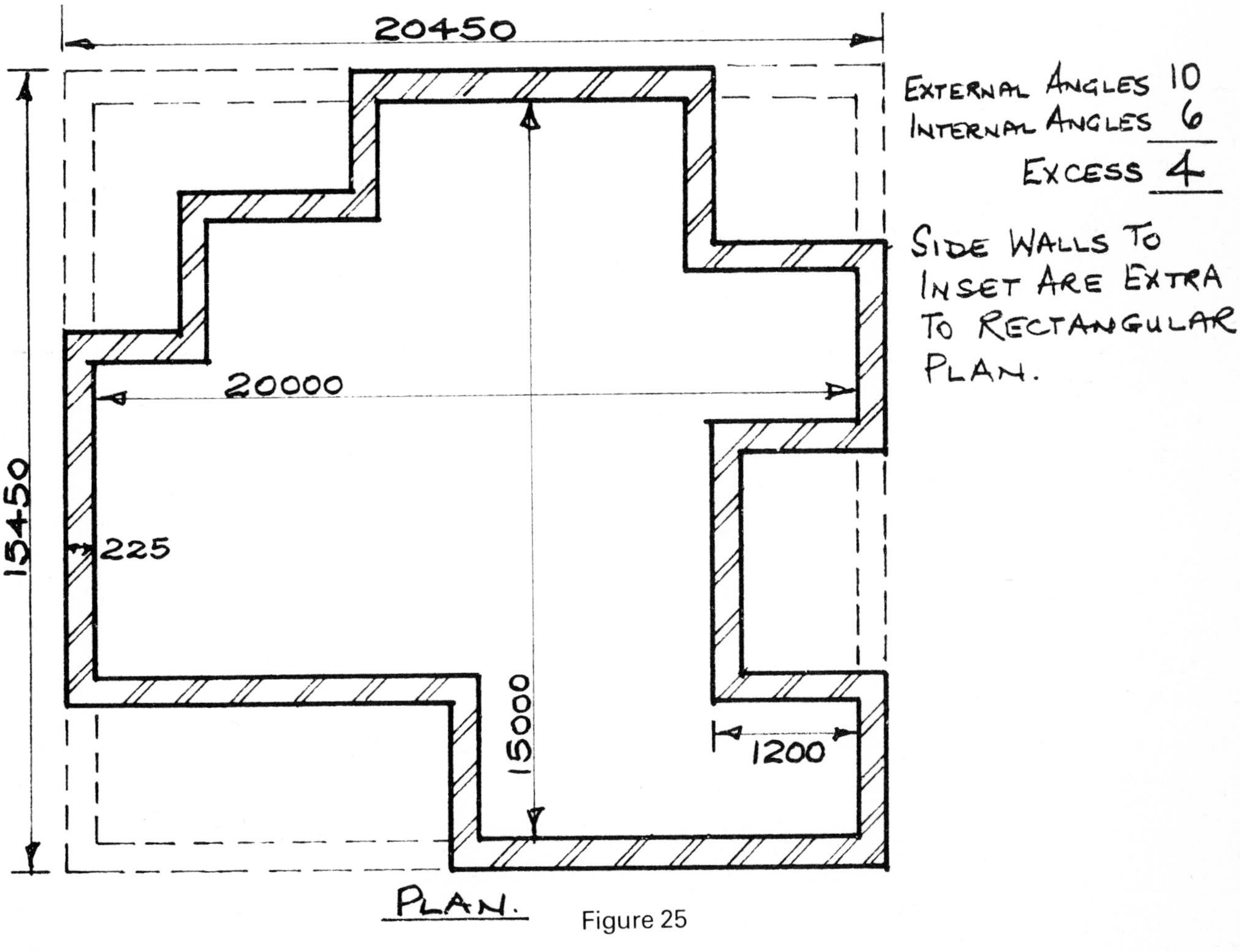

20450
EXTERNAL ANGLES 10
INTERNAL ANGLES 6
EXCESS 4
SIDE WALLS TO INSET ARE EXTRA TO RECTANGULAR PLAN.
20000
15450
225
15000
1200
PLAN.

Figure 25

Method A

length		20.000
width		15.000
	2/	
		35.000
insets 2/		70.000
1.200		2.400
Internal perimeter		72.400
Add external angles	4/	
	0.225	0.900
Mean length		73.300

Method B

length		20.450
width		15.450
	2/	
		35.900
		71.800
insets 2/		
1.200		2.400
External perimeter		74.200
Ddt. external angles	4/	
	0.225	0.900
Mean Length		73.300

Method C

length		20.450
width		15.000
insets		1.200
	2/	
		36.650
Mean length		73.300

Where the brickwork is not of uniform thickness for the full height of the wall the mean length of each section of wall must be calculated separately.

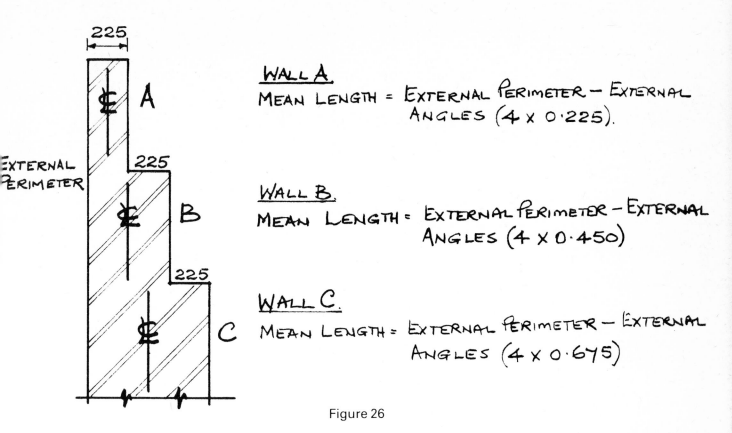

WALL A.
MEAN LENGTH = EXTERNAL PERIMETER – EXTERNAL ANGLES (4 x 0·225).

WALL B.
MEAN LENGTH = EXTERNAL PERIMETER – EXTERNAL ANGLES (4 X 0·450)

WALL C.
MEAN LENGTH = EXTERNAL PERIMETER – EXTERNAL ANGLES (4 x 0·675)

Figure 26

In cases where the foundation is stepped the minimum height of brickwork is measured for the mean length of the wall and the additional height of brickwork between steps measured separately.

WALL INTERSECTIONS

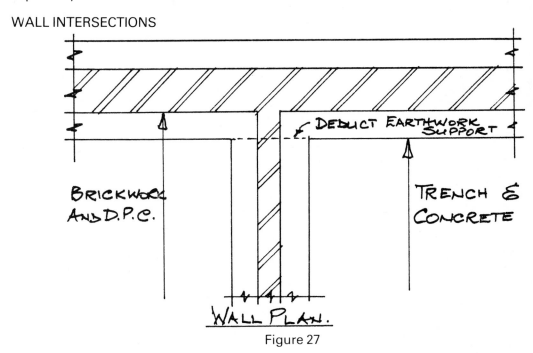

BRICKWORK AND D.P.C.

DEDUCT EARTHWORK SUPPORT

TRENCH & CONCRETE

WALL PLAN.

Figure 27

The main wall and foundations are measured complete so that the dimensions for earthwork support must be adjusted at trench intersections. The intersecting wall and foundations are measured between the main walls as Figure 27.

SURFACE WATER. An item for keeping the surface of the site and the excavations free of surface water must always be included (SMM D25). No reference to this item need be made during taking off as it is later incorporated by the worker up.

Plate 1
SIMPLE FOUNDATION 'A'

S.M.M. RULES	SECTION A	
	D.9.11.13.14.15.16.17.29.31.33.34.35.36.37.40.43.	
	F.3.4.5.6.	
	G.3.4.5.14.37.	

APPROACH:-

Topsoil excavation
Foundation trenches
Concrete foundation
Walls
Damp-proof course
Facework
Reinstatement
Hardcore filling
Concrete bed
Damp-proof membrane

The sequence of measurement follows
closely the order of construction.

S.M.M. D9.
Topsoil which is to be preserved –
otherwise S.M.M. D13.

Measure topsoil excavation to
outside edge of conc. foundation.

```
            conc foln    0.725
                wall     0.225
                     2 ) 0.500
                   fpd = 0.250
                         5.000
    walls 2/0.225        0.450
    fpd   2/0.250        0.500
              L =        5.950
                         3.000
                         0.450
                         0.500
              W =        3.950
```

5.95	Exc topsoil	150 mm deep topsoil excavation is
3.95	avg. 150mm dp.	sufficient to remove vegetable
		matter and reduces level to
		underside of hardcore filling.

5.95	Deposit preserved	S.M.M. D31.
3.95	topsoil in temp.	
0.15	spoil heap avg.	
	25m from exc.	

This mean length must be carefully
checked since it is used in the
measurement of several items.

```
              5.000
              3.000
         2/   8.000
      INTL =  16.000
Angles 4/0.225  0.900
 MEAN LENGTH. 16.900
```

Width of trench as conc. foundation.

```
               0.600
   Conc fdn    0.225
               0.825
   topsoil     0.150
         D =   0.675
```

16.90	Exc tr to rec. fdns
0.73	stg R.L. max
0.68	depth n.e. 1.00 m

&

Filling to exc
wi matl arising
from the exc

S.M.M. D33.34.35.
Assume whole of trench is filled in
the first instance and then Ddt.
volume of filling displaced when
measuring conc. & bkwk in trench.

S.M.M. D14.15.16.17.
Dimensions as topsoil.

```
              5.950
              3.950
         2/   9.900
             19.800
```

19.80	Earthwork support
0.15	max depth n.e.
2/16.90	1.00 m & n.e.
0.68	2.00 m between
	opposing faces

Topsoil.

Trench – twice times mean length X
depth.

| 16.90 | Level & comp |
| 0.73 | bot exc |

S.M.M. D40.
Mean length X width of trench

S.M.M. F3.4.5.6.

16.90	Conc (1:2:4) fdns in
0.73	trenches 150-300 mm
0.23	thk poured agst
	face of exc

Mean length of trench X width X
thickness of concrete.

Particulars of materials given in
Preamble in preference to description.

&

Ddt Filling exc ab

&

Add Remove exc
matl from site

S.M.M. D29.

31

	Wall 0.600
	0.150
	H = 0.750

16.90
0.75

One bk wall in c.b. laid Eng bond in ct. mor (1:3) in fdns

S.M.M. G3.4.5.

Size of bricks given in Preamble in preference to description.

Proj 1/4 Bk = 56 mm
1/2 Bk = 112.5mm

2/16.90
0.08

Proj of footgs 56 mm thk in c.b. ditto.

&

Ditto 112.5 mm thk in c.b. ditto

Trench 0.675
Conc 0.225
0.450

S.M.M. G5.

WALL

PROJECTIONS
1/4 BK
1/2 BK

Volume of brickwork in the trench.

16.90
0.23
0.45

Ddt
Filling to exc a.b.

&

2/16.90
0.06
0.08

Add
Remove exc matl from site

2/16.90
0.11
0.08

S.M.M. G37.
Mean length of wall.

16.90

One layer hessian based bit: felt roz D.P.C. whg 3.8 kg/m² 225mm wide bedd in ct. mor (1:3) no allowce made for laps.

MEAN L = 16.900
Angles 4/0.225 = 0.900
EXTL = 17.800

GL - DPC = 0.150
below GL = 0.075
0.225

S.M.M. G14.

Usually measured one course below general G.L. to allow for surface irregularities.

17.80 0.23	E.O. c.b. for facewk in Messrs Downings Heather Rustic feg bks laid Eng bond & ptd wi neat w/s jt in fdns	Size of bricks and composition of mortar NOT different from those in the body of the work and not included in the description.

REINSTATE

Facewk 17.800
Spd 4/0.250 1.000
          18.800

In many cases this will not be measured since further excavation may be required for paths, paved areas etc.

18.80 0.25 0.15	Ddt Remove exc matl from site & Add Filling to exc ab.

5.00 3.00	Hardcore filling to make up levels avg 150 mm thk levelled, compacted & blinded wi ashes incl level & compact bot. exc.

S.M.M. D33.36.40.43.

5.00 3.00 0.15	Conc (1:2:4) bed 100 – 150 mm thk laid on hardcore

S.M.M. F4.5.6.
Particulars of materials given in Preamble in preference to description.

5.00 3.00	Trowel surface finish on conc & One layer "Bituthene" self-adhesive loz D.P.M. on conc no allowce made for laps.

S.M.M. F9.

S.M.M. G37.
Alternatively – may be measured with floor screeds.

Plate 1
SIMPLE FOUNDATION 'A'

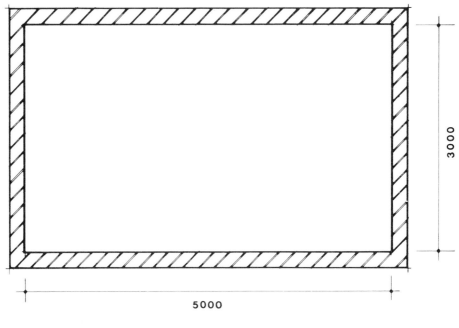

3000

5000

PLAN   Scale. 1 : 50.

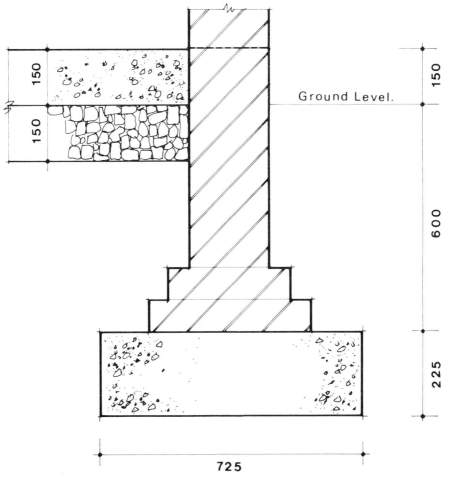

150

150

150

Ground Level.

600

225

725

SECTION   Scale. 1 : 10.

Concrete (1 : 2 : 4)
Cement Mortar (1 : 3)
Hessian based Bituminous Felt d.p.c. 3.8 kg/m²
Bitu-Thene self adhesive damp-proof membrane.

Common Bricks - English Bond.
Messrs. G. H. Downing and Co. Ltd. -
Heather Rustic Facing Bricks.

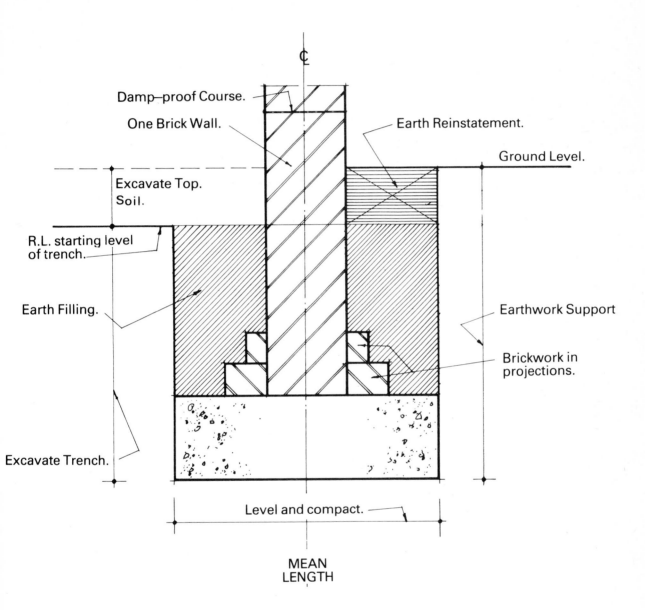

Damp–proof Course.

One Brick Wall.

Earth Reinstatement.

Ground Level.

Excavate Top. Soil.

R.L. starting level of trench.

Earth Filling.

Earthwork Support

Brickwork in projections.

Excavate Trench.

Level and compact.

MEAN LENGTH

MEAN LENGTH used to measure:–

Trench Excavation and Disposal.
Earthwork Support.
Level and Compact.
Concrete Foundations.
One Brick Wall.
Projecting Footings.
Damp–proof Course.
Items above D.P.C.

Plate 2
SIMPLE FOUNDATION 'B'

S.M.M. RULES

SECTION A
    D.9.11.13.14.15.16.17.29.30.33.34.35.36.40.43.
    F.3.4.5.6.
    G.3.4.5.9.14.37.
    V.1.3.4.

APPROACH:-

Topsoil excavation
Foundation trenches
Concrete foundation
External walls
Cavity filling
Internal walls
Damp-proof course
Facings
Reinstatement
Hardcore filling
Concrete bed
Damp-proof membrane

The sequence of measurement follow
closely the order of construction.

Conc fdn	0·600
wall	0·275
2)	0·325
Spd =	0·163

S.M.M. D9.
Topsoil which is to be preserved -
otherwise S.M.M. D13.

		7·200
Spd ²/0·163		0·326
L =		7·526

Measure topsoil excavation to
outside edge on conc. foundation.

	6·300
	0·326
W =	6·626

7·53	
6·63	

Exc topsoil
avg 150 mm dp
&
Preserved topsoil
spread on site
as filling to make
up levels avg
150 mm thk.

150 mm deep topsoil excavation is
sufficient to remove vegetable
matter.

S.M.M. D30.36.

EXTR WALLS

	7·200
	6·300
2	13·500
EXTR =	27·000
Angles ⁴/0·275	1·100
MEAN LENGTH =	25·900

S.M.M. D11.13.
The mean length must be carefully
checked since it is used in the
measurement of several items.

Width of trench as conc. foundatio

GL. 5.150
     5.200
     5.200
     5.150
  4)20.700
Avg GL = 5.175
Topsoil 0.150
Avg RL = 5.025
u/s conc fdn 4.545
trench = 0.450

INTL WALLS

Conc fdn 0.413
   wall 0.113
   2)0.300
Spd   0.150
      6.300
Walls 2/0.275 0.550
      5.750
      3.000
Bkk & DPC = 8.450

Spd EXTL
Walls 3/0.163=0.489
INTL WALL 0.150=0.639
TRENCH & CONC = 8.111

Average depth of trench for external walls is also sufficiently accurate for the internal walls.

25.90		
0.60		
0.45		
8.11		
0.41		
0.45		

Exc tr to rec fdns stg R.L. max depth n.e. 1.00 m
&
Filling to exc ws matl arising from the exc

S.M.M. D33.34.35.
Assume whole of trench is filled in the first instance and then Ddt. volume of filling displaced when measuring conc. & bkwk. in trench.

      4.526
      6.626
   2)14.152
     28.304

S.M.M. D15.16.17.
Dimensions as topsoil excavation.

28.30		
0.15		
2/25.90		
0.45		
2/8.11		
0.45		

Earthwork support max depth n.e. 1.00 m & n.e. 2.00m between opposing faces

Topsoil.

Trench - Extl. wall - twice times mean length X depth.

Trench - Intl wall - twice times mean length X depth.

3/ 0·41 0·45	D<u>oll</u> Ditto		Intersection of trenches.
			<u>S.M.M.</u> D40. Mean length X width of trench.
25·90 0·60 8·11 0·41	Level & comp. bot exc		
25·90 0·60 0·23 8·11 0·41 0·23	Conc (1:2:4) fdns in trenches 150 - 300 mm thk poured agst faces of exc &		<u>S.M.M.</u> F3.4.5.6. Mean length of trench X width X thickness of concrete. Particulars of materials given in Preamble in preference to description
	D<u>oll</u> Filling to exc ab & <u>Add</u> Remove exc matl from site		<u>S.M.M.</u> D29.
	EXT. WALLS FFL 5·400 floor fin <u>0·050</u> DPC level 5·350 U/S Conc fdn <u>4·575</u> 0·775 Conc fdn 0·225 WALL = <u>0·550</u>		<u>S.M.M.</u> G3.4.5.
2/ 25·90 0·55	H.B. skin of hollow wall in c.b. laid stretcher bond in c. mor (1:3) in fdns.		Size of bricks given in Preamble in preference to description.
	WALL 0·275 Skins <u>0·225</u> Cavity <u>0·050</u>		<u>S.M.M.</u> G9. Mean length of external wall X height of brickwork.
25·90 0·55	forming cavities 50 mm wide in hollow wall		wall ties not required.

		wall 0.550	S.M.M. F6.
		less 0.100	
		0.450	

25.90	Conc (1:2:4) filling
0.05	to hollow wall
0.45	n.e. 100 mm thk

Particulars of materials given in
Preamble in preference to description.

INTL
WALLS

S.M.M. G3.4.5.
Mean length of internal wall X height
of brickwork.

8.75	H.B. wall in c.b.
0.55	laid stretcher
	bond in ct mot
	(1:3) in fdns.

Size of bricks given in Preamble in
preference to description.

trench 0.450
Conc 0.225
0.225

25.90	Ddt.
0.28	Filling to exc ab
0.23	#

Volume of brickwork in the trench

8.75	Add
0.11	Remove exc matl
0.23	a.b.

S.M.M. G37.
Mean length of walls.

2/25.90	One layer hessian
8.75	based bit felt
	lay. D.P.C. wkg
	3.8 kg/m² 112.5 mm
	wide ledd in
	ct mot (1:3) no
	allowce made for
	laps.

Extl 27.000
Rgles 4/0.113 0.452
26.548

Mean length of external skin

DPC level 5.350
Avg. GL. 5.175
0.175
below GL 0.075
0.250

Usually measured one course below
general G.L. to allow for surface
irregularities.

Ddt Commons,
ADD FACINGS
G.L.

26·55 0·25	<u>Ddt</u> H.B. skin hollow wall in c.b. & <u>Add</u> H.B. skin hollow wall entirely messrs Downings Heather Rustic fcg bks laid stretcher bond in ct·mort(1:3) & ptd in neat w/s jt in fdns.	<u>S.M.M. G3.14.</u> Size of bricks given in Preamble in preference to description.

	<u>REINSTATE</u> EXTL 27·000 Spd 4/0·163 0·652 27·652	In many cases this will not be measured since further excavation may be required for paths, paved areas etc.
27·65 0·16 0·15	<u>Ddt</u> Remove exc matl ab & <u>Add</u> Filling to exc ab.	

walls 2/0·275 4·200
        0·550
INTL = 6·650
        6·300
        0·550
        5·750
	<u>S.M.M. D33.34.36.40.43.</u>

FFL 5·400
<u>LESS</u>
floor fin 0·050
Conc bed 0·100 0·150
u/s conc bed = 5·250
Avg R.L = 5·025
Avg fill = 0·225

6·65
5·75
	Hardcore filling to
	make up levels avg
	225mm thk, levelled
	compacted & blinded
	in ashes incl
	level & compact
	bottom of Exc
		Reduced level at each corner lower
		than 5.250 therefore whole of site
		area is to be filled.
		Maximum depth of filling will occur
		at lowest corner.
		      Lowest corner G.L. 5.150
		           Topsoil. <u>0.150</u>
		             R.L. 5.000
		   u/s conc. bed <u>5.250</u>
		     Max. filling 0.250
		Therefore all filling m²

40

6.65 5.75 0.15	Conc (1:2:4) bed 100-150 mm thk laid on hardcore	S.M.M. F4.5.6. Particulars of materials given in Preamble in preference to description.
	. . .	
6.65 5.75	Trowel surface finish on conc	S.M.M. F9.
	& Prepare & two coats	S.M.M. V1.3.4. Liquid application similar to Painting
	"Synthaprufe" on conc floor & blind surface wi sharp sand 1 m²	Alternatively - may be measured with floor screeds.
8.75 0.11	Ddt. Hardcore filling avg 225 mm thk ab. &.	Mean length X thickness of internal wall.
	Add. Two coats "Synthaprufe" ab.	
8.75 0.11 0.15	Add Conc (1:2:4) bed 100 - 150 mm thk ab.	

Plate 2
SIMPLE FOUNDATION 'B'

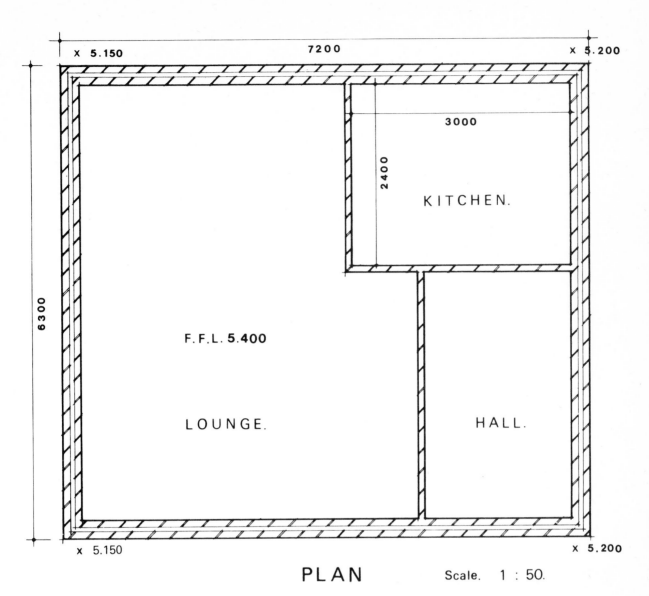

PLAN   Scale.   1 : 50.

SECTION

All Concrete (1:2:4)
Cement Mortar (1:3)
Common Bricks—Stretcher Bond.
Messrs. G.H.Downing and Co. Ltd.
Heather Rustic Facing Bricks.
Bituminous felt D.P.C. weighing 3.3 kg/m.
Damp—proof membrane,two coats
''Synthaprufe.''
Top soil spread and levelled
over site.

Scale.   1 : 20.

Plate 3
SIMPLE FOUNDATION 'C'

S.M.M. RULES			SECTION A			

SECTION A
      D.11.12.13.29.33.34.35.36.40.
      F.3.4.5.6.9.12.13.14.
      G.3.4.5.9.14.37.
      V.1.3.4.

APPROACH:-

Reduce level excavation
R.C. raft foundation
Walls
Cavity filling
Damp-proof course
Reinstatement
Hardcore filling
Concrete bed
Damp-proof membrane

The sequence of measurement follows closely the order of construction.

S.M.M. D11.13.
Topsoil not preserved.

```
                        5.000
walls 2/0.245  0.550
skd  2/0.300   0.600
       Raft =   6.150
                3.000
                0.550
                0.600
        W =     4.150
```

Measure reduce level excavation to outside edge of foundation.

```
6.15
4.15
0.23
```

Exc to reduce
levels max depth
n.e. 0.25m

&

Filling to exc wi
matl arising from
the exc.

S.M.M. D33.34.35.
Assume whole of foundation is filled in first instance and then Ddt. volume of filling displaced by con bkwk. and hardcore below G.L.
Earthwork support not required –
S.M.M. D15.
S.M.M. D11.12.
Assume nature of ground requires u of formwork to edge of foundation.

```
                6.150
                4.150
          2/   10.300
 Formwk = 20.600
wk. sp 4/0.250 =  1.000
  MEAN GIRTH = 21.600
```

Formwork not exceeding one metre deep working space as S.M.M. D12.

```
21.60
0.25
0.23
```

Exc workg space
and exc to reduce
levels max depth
n.e. 0.25m & fill
wkg space wi
matl arising from
exc.

6.15 4.15 0.15	Being conc (1:2:4) bed 100-150 mm thk laid on earth

S.M.M. F3.4.5.6.
Particulars of materials given in preamble in preference to description.

6.15 4.15	Level & compact bot exc & Tamped surface fin on conc

S.M.M. D40.
Length X width of bed.

S.M.M. F9.

S.M.M. F12.

$$6.150$$
Conc cover 2/0.050 0.100
$$L = 6.050$$
$$4.150$$
$$0.100$$
$$W = 4.050$$

6.05 4.05	Steel fabric reinf 100 x 200 mm mesh whg 3.05 kg/m² wi 150 mm side & end laps in ground slab.

S.M.M. F12.

$$5.000$$
$$3.000$$
2/ 8.000
INTL = 16.000
Angles 4/0.275 = 1.100
MEAN LENGTH = 17.100
$$0.275$$
2/0.250 = 0.500
$$W = 0.775$$

Fabric strip located on centre-line under walls. Use mean length of walls for measurement of fabric strip, forming cavities and cavity filling.

17.10	Ditto in strip 775 mm wide in one width wi main bars longitudinal and 150 mm end laps in ditto

20·60	Fwk edge of bed n.e. 250 mm high	S.M.M. F13.14.
	$$\begin{aligned} \text{INTᴸ} &= 16.000 \\ \text{Angles } 4/0.113 &= 0.452 \\ \text{MEAN LENGTH} &= 16.452 \end{aligned}$$	S.M.M. G3.4.5. Mean length of internal skin X height.
	$$\begin{aligned} \text{H'core} &\quad 0.150 \\ \text{Conc} &\quad 0.100 \\ \text{WALL} &\quad 0.250 \end{aligned}$$	
16·45 0·25	H.B. skin hollow wall in c.b. laid stretcher bond in ct. mor (1:3) in fdns	Size of bricks given in Preamble in preference to description.
	$$\begin{aligned} \text{INTᴸ} &= 16.000 \\ \text{Angles } 3/4/0.275 &= 2.200 \\ \text{EXTᴸ} &= 18.200 \\ \text{Angles } 4/0.113 &= 0.452 \\ \text{MEAN LENGTH} &= 17.748 \end{aligned}$$	S.M.M. G3.14. Mean length of external skin X height which allows one course below general G.L. for surface irregularities.
17·75 0·25	H.B. skin hollow wall entirely Messrs Downings Heather Rustic facg bks laid stretcher bond in ct mor (1:3) & ptd wi neat w/s jt in fdns.	Size of bricks given in Preamble in preference to description.
	$$\begin{aligned} \text{WALL} &\quad 0.275 \\ \text{HB skins} &\quad 0.225 \\ \text{Cavity} &\quad 0.050 \end{aligned}$$	S.M.M. G9. Mean length of walls X height of brickwork.
17·10 0·25	Form cavities 50 mm wide in hollow wall	Wall ties not required.
	$$\begin{aligned} \text{WALL} &\quad 0.250 \\ \text{less} &\quad 0.100 \\ \hline &\quad 0.150 \end{aligned}$$	S.M.M. F5.6.
17·10 0·05 0·15	conc (1:2:4) filling to hollow wall n.e. 100 mm thk.	Particulars of materials given in Preamble in preference to description.

2/14.10		

One layer hessian based bit. felt lay D.P.C. whg 3.8 kg/m². 112·5mm wide bedd in et mor (1:3) no allowce made for laps.

S.M.M. G37.
Twice X mean length of walls.

```
            Exc   0.225
      Core bed   0.150
               ───────
                0.075
```

Consider further excavation or filling for paths, paved ares etc.

6.15	
4.15	
0.15	

Ddt
Filling to exc ab.
&

R.C. bed.

5.55	
3.55	
0.08	

Add
Remove exc matl from site

Overall dimensions of brickwork.

S.M.M. D29.

S.M.M. D33, 34, 36, 40.

| 5.00 | |
| 3.00 | |

Hardcore filling to make up levels avg 150 mm thk levelled, compacted & blinded wi' ashes

5.00	
3.00	
0.10	

Conc (1:2:4) bed 100 - 150 mm thk laid on hardcore

S.M.M. F4, 5, 6.
Particulars of materials given in Preamble in preference to description.

| 5.00 | |
| 3.00 | |

Trowel surface finish on conc
&
Prepare & two coats "Synthaprufe" on conc floor & blind surface wi' sharp sand

S.M.M. F9.

S.M.M. V1, 3, 4.
Liquid application similar to painting.

Alternatively - may be measured with floor screeds.

/NTL

Plate 3
SIMPLE FOUNDATION 'C'

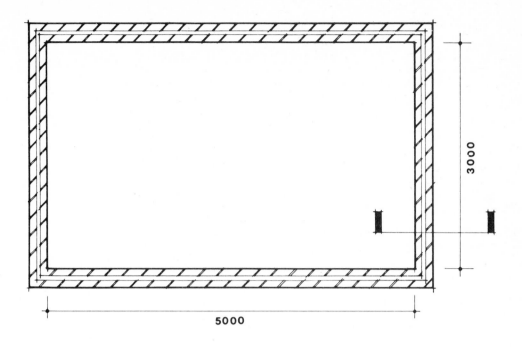

3000

5000

PLAN   Scale. 1 : 50.

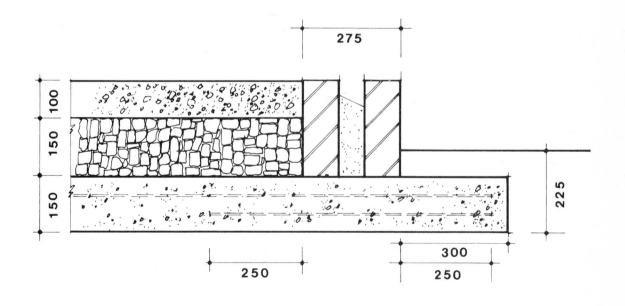

275

100

150

150

225

250

300

250

SECTION

All Concrete (1 : 2 : 4).
Fabric Reinforcement 100 x 200 mesh weighing
3.05 kg/m^2 with 150mm laps.
Common Brickwork Stretcher Bond
Messrs. G. H. Downing and Co. Ltd., Heather Rustic Facing Bricks.
Cement mortar (1 : 3).
Hessian based Bituminous Felt D.P.C. weighing 3.8 kg/m^2
Damp - proof membrane two coats "Synthaprufe."

Scale. 1 : 10.

Chapter IV

Structural Walls

Approach

(1) Divide complex buildings into units of manageable size. Where a large project includes several buildings measure each as a separate unit.

(2) Measure walls over all openings, recesses, projections and similar features which can be more easily dealt with by separate adjustment.

(3) The taker off must apply his knowledge of construction technology to determine the sequence of construction which, in most cases, will provide a logical sequence of measurement.

(4) Each building unit must be considered on its merits but a typical sequence of measurement would be:

EXTERNAL WALLS	Brickwork and associated labours.
	Brick facework and associated labours.
INTERNAL WALLS	Brickwork and associated labours.
	Brick facework and associated labours.
CHIMNEY BREAST	Brickwork and associated labours.
	Brick facework and associated labours.
CHIMNEY STACK	Brickwork and associated labours.
	Brick facework and associated labours.
FIRE OPENINGS AND FLUES	Opening/lintel/flue lining/chimney pots.

Measurement of brickwork

(1) Brickwork in this group shall be classified as either load bearing or non-load bearing superstructure and each given under an appropriate heading.

(2) Brickwork and blockwork are measured the mean length by the average height. Fair face or facework is measured on the exposed face (SMM G4).

(3) The height of the walls should be measured up to some convenient general level, e.g. eaves level, and adjustments made for gables, parapets, higher or lower eaves, etc.

(4) Half brick walls and one brick walls built fair both sides or entirely of facings shall each be given separately in square metres (SMM G14). All other walls are measured in common brickwork and any facework measured as extra over.

(5) Where only part of a half brick wall is built fair both sides or entirely of facings it is often easier to measure the whole wall as common brickwork in the first instance, followed by an appropriate adjustment.

Fires and vents

Chimney breasts and chimney stacks are part of the structural brickwork and should be measured with the walls. Fireplace openings and flue linings may be measured either with the walls or with fires and vents. All other work associated with the fireplace should be measured in the fires and vents group. The measurement of fires may be divided into:

(a) Stoves, grates and fixing.
(b) Fireplace opening (unless measured with walls).
(c) Surrounds, hearths and similar units.
(d) Flue (unless measured with walls).

Stoves, grates, surrounds, hearths and similar units are each enumerated separately giving particulars of any assembling, jointing and setting required (SMM G56). The choice of unit is often made by the client at a later stage in the contract and therefore the supply of such units is usually covered by a prime cost sum with a separate item for fixing. Should any unit require an air duct this would be measured immediately after the unit.

Electric or gas heaters and all associated work are usually measured in the appropriate services group.

Forming openings in walls and providing and building in air bricks and the like shall each be enumerated separately (SMM G52). Air bricks necessary for the ventilation of timber ground floors are usually measured with the floor and all others with fires and vents.

Blockwork and rubble walling

The measurement of blockwork and rubble walling follows the same procedure as used for brickwork subject only to the minor variations in the rules of measurement.

Plate 4
SCREEN WALL & PIERS

S.M.M. RULES		

SECTION A
D.11.13.14.15.16.17.29.33.34.35.40.
F.3.4.5.6.
G.3.4.5.14.21.22.37.

APPROACH:-

Foundation trench & pit
Concrete foundations
Brickwork up to d.p.c.
Damp-proof course
Facework below d.p.c.
Brickwork above d.p.c.
Facework and copings
Reinstatement

The sequence of measurement follows
closely the order of construction.

Conc foln 0·525
wall 0·225
2) 0·300
Spd = 0·150

S.M.M. D11.13.

wall 1·200
wall 1·100
pier 0·450
Spd 2/0·150 = 0·300
L = 3·050

Straight sections of wall.

0·225
0·225
D = 0·450

Width of trench as conc. foundation.

pier 0·450
Spd 2/0·150 = 0·300
L = 0·750

3·05		
0·53		
0·45		
2/0·75		
0·11		
0·45		

Exc tr to rec fdns stg G.L. max depth n.e. 1.00m

Filling to exc mi matl arising from exc

Pier projections.

S.M.M. D33.34.35.

TRENCH
750
113
113
PROJECTIONS

1/4/2/3½/		
1·00		
0·53		
0·45		

Exc curved tr to rec fdns stg G.L. max dp n.e. 1.00m

Filling to exc ab.

S.M.M. D11.13.

No distinction between straight
and curved work.

52

	Isol pier 0.450 Spa 2/0.150 0.300 L & W = 0.750	S.M.M. D11.13. Depth as for trench.
0.75 0.75 0.45	Exc pit to rec base of isolated pier stg G.L. max depth n.e. 1.00m both plan dimensions less than 1.25m (Pn No 1) & Filling to exc ab.	
2/3.05 0.45	Earthwork support max depth n.e. 1.00m & n.e. 2.00m between opposing faces	S.M.M. D11.15.16.17. Twice times length X depth of trench.
0.75 0.45		Pier end.
2/0.11 0.45		Pier returns.
4/0.75 0.45		Length of each side X depth of pit.
0.53 0.45		End of trench – This item could be considered as over 4.00m between opposing faces.
2/4/2/3½/1.00 0.45	Curved earthwork support ditto	S.M.M. D14.15.16.17. Twice times length X depth of curved trench.
3.05 0.53	Level & compact bot exc.	S.M.M. D40. Length X width of trench.
2/0.75 0.11		Pier projections.
4/2/3½/1.00 0.53		Length X width of curved trench.
0.75 0.75		Isolated pier.

53

	3.05 0.53 0.23	Conc (1:2:4) fdns in trenches 150 – 300 mm thk poured agst face of exc	S.M.M. F3.4.5.6. Length of trench X width and thickness of concrete. Particulars of materials given in Preamble in preference to description.
2/	0.75 0.11 0.23	&	
¼/2/3¼/	1.00 0.53 0.23	Ddt Filling to exc ab &	No distinction between straight and curved work.
		Add Remove exc matl from site	S.M.M. D29.
	0.75 0.75 0.23	Conc (1:2:4) isolated fdn base to pier 150 – 300 mm thk poured agst face of exc (In No 1) &	S.M.M. F3.4.5.6. Particulars of materials given in Preamble in preference to description.
		Ddt. Filling to exc ab &	
		Add Remove exc matl from site	
		wall 1.200 wall 1.100 pier 0.450 L = 2.750	S.M.M. G3.4.5. Measure wall and piers in common bricks then adjust for facing bricks or facework.
		Conc – GL 0.225 GL – DPc 0.100 0.325	
	2.75 0.33	One bk wall in cb laid Flemish bond in mortar (1:1:6) in fdns	Size of bricks given in Preamble in preference to description.
¼/2/3¼/	1.00 0.33	Ditto curved to 1000 mm mean radius	S.M.M. G3.4.5. G4 – Curved work.

2/ 0·33	Projections 450 mm wide 112.5 mm dp in cb. ab.	S.M.M. G5. Projections.

WALL
112·5mm
PROJECTIONS

0·45 0·33	Two brick isolated pier in cb. ab.

S.M.M. G5.
Isolated piers.

2/ 0·45 0·45	One layer hessian based bit. felt bog. D.P.C. whg 3·8 kg/m² bedd in mortar (1:1:6) no allowce made for laps

S.M.M. G37.
Piers.

1·20 1·10	Ditto 225 mm wide

Straight wall.

3/ 1·00	Ditto 225 mm wide curved incl cuttg to curve.

Curved wall.

0·100
0·075
0·175

Facing bricks usually measured one
course below general G.L. to allow
for surface irregularities.

1·20 0·18 1·10 0·18	Ddt One bk wall in cb. in fdns &

Straight wall.

Add One bk wall entirely Phorpres Tuscan fcg bks laid Flemish bond in mor (1:1:6) + ptd b.s. wi neat w/s jt in fdns.

S.M.M. G14.
Size of facing bricks given in Preamble
in preference to description.

55

0·18	Fair return one bk wide in fdns.

S.M.M. G14.

¼/2/37½/	1.00	**Ddt.**	Curved work.
	0.18	One bk wall in	
		c.b. curved to	
		1000 mm rad	
		&	
		Add	S.M.M. G4.14.
		One bk wall	
		entirely fcg bks	
		a.b. curved to	
		1000 mm mean	
		radius in fdns.	
			S.M.M. G14.
			Piers over one brick thick,
3/	0.45	E.O. c.b. for facewk	therefore not entirely facings.
	0.18	in Phorpres Tuscan	
		fcg bks laid	
4/	0.45	Flemish bond &	
	0.18	ptd wi neat	
		w/s jt in fdns	
2/	0.18	Facewk to margins	S.M.M. G14.

The following in non-loadbearing superstructure

S.M.M. G3.
Use of heading saves repetition in writing descriptions.

	1.20	One bk wall	
	0.90	entirely fcg	Straight wall.
	1.10	bks a.b.	
	0.90		
	0.90	Fair return one bk	
		wide	
¼/2/37½/	1.00	One bk wall	Curved work.
	0.90	entirely fcg bks	
		a.b. curved to	
		1000 mm mean	
		radius	

0.45		One brick wall in	S.M.M. G3.4.5.
0.90		c.b. laid Flemish bond a.b.	
		ATTACHED PIER.	
2/0.45		Projections 450mm	S.M.M. G5.
0.90		wide 112.5mm dp in c.b. ditto	
		ISOL. PIER	S.M.M. G5.
		1.000	
		0.300	
		1.300	
		GL–DPC 0.100	
		1.200	
0.45		Two brick	attach pier becomes isolated pier for 300mm above wall.
0.30		isolated pier	
0.45		in c.b. a.b.	Isolated pier.
1.20			
		FACEWK TO PIERS.	S.M.M. G14. Attached pier.
3/0.45		E.O. c.b. for	
1.20		facewk a.b.	Attached pier above wall.
0.45			
0.30			Isolated pier.
4/0.45			
1.20			
			S.M.M. G14.
2/0.90		Facewk to margins a.b	
			S.M.M. G21.
1.20		Hog. copg entirely	Straight wall.
1.10		Rhorpres Tuscan fcg bks 225mm on bed 112.5mm high formed all headers on edge b & p in mor (1:1:6).	

57

ᴸ/4/2/3½/	1·00	Ditto curved to 1000 mm mean radius	S.M.M. G4. Curved work.
	2	End copg $\oint$	S.M.M. A4 – Junctions between straight and curved work deemed to be included. S.M.M. G21.
		Capping to isol pier size 450×450mm entirely Sharpres Tuscan fcg bks 112·5 mm high formed all headers on edge ab.	S.M.M. G22.

(END NON LOADBEARING)
SUPERSTRUCTURE

			S.M.M. D33.34.35. Volume of brickwork in trench.
2·75		Ddt.	Straight wall.
0·23		Filling to exc ab	
0·23		$\oint$	
ᴸ/4/2/3½/	1·00		Curved wall.
0·23			
0·23			
2/0·45		Add	Pier projections.
0·11		Remove exc	
0·23		matl ab	
0·45			Isolated pier.
0·45			
0·23			S.M.M. D29.

58

Plate 4
SCREEN WALL &PIERS

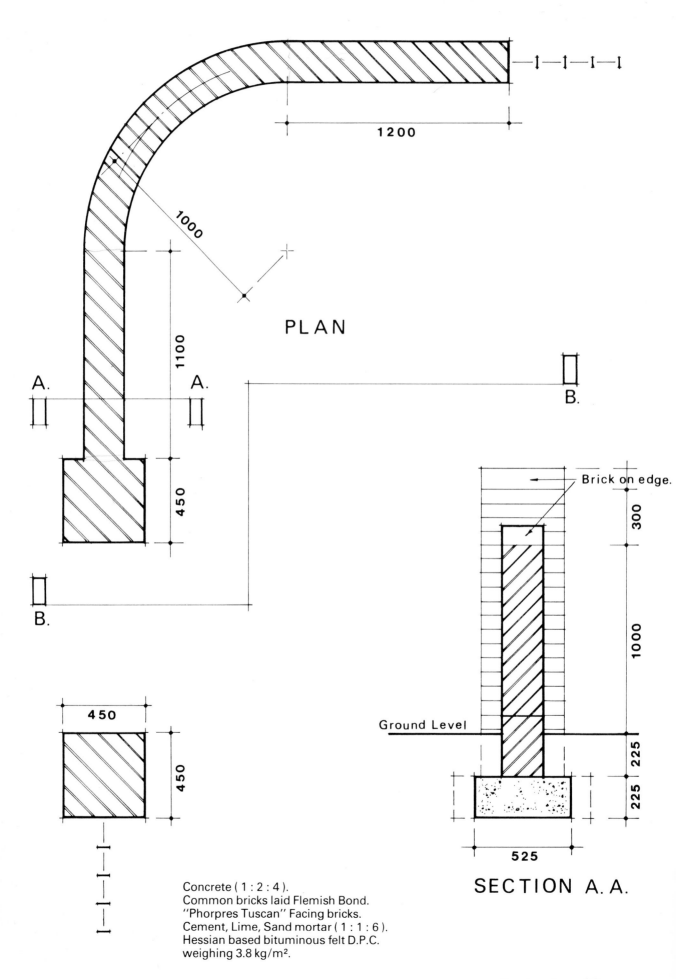

PLAN

1200

1000

1100

450

A.   A.

B.

450

450

B.

SECTION A.A.

Brick on edge.

300

1000

Ground Level

225

225

225

525

Concrete (1 : 2 : 4).
Common bricks laid Flemish Bond.
"Phorpres Tuscan" Facing bricks.
Cement, Lime, Sand mortar (1 : 1 : 6).
Hessian based bituminous felt D.P.C.
weighing 3.8 kg/m².

Scale. 1 : 20

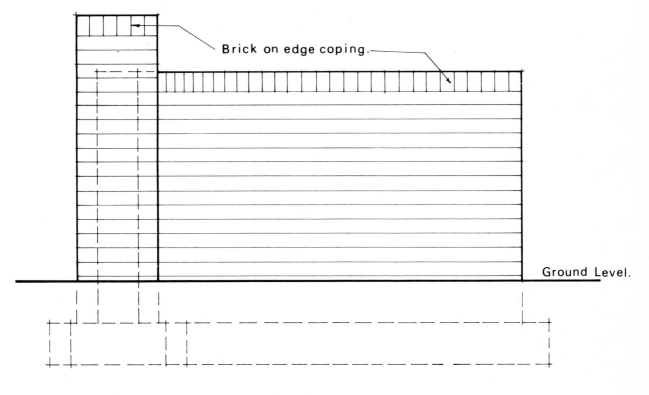

Brick on edge coping.

Ground Level.

ELEVATION B.B.

Plate 5
BRICK WALLS & CHIMNEY STACK

S.M.M. RULES   SECTION A
              F.18.21.
              G.3.4.5.9.14.53.55.

APPROACH:-   External walls
              Party wall
              Chimney breasts & stack
              Fire-openings & flues

The following in
load-bearing superstructure

             Use of heading saves repetition
             in writing descriptions.

           EXTL
           WALLS   S.M.M. G3.14.
           12.000
            7.200
        2/ 19.200
     EXTL = 38.400
     angles
     4/0.113   0.452
   MEAN LENGTH 37.948

        GF 2.400
       floor 0.225
        FF. 2.400
          5.025
      less 0.225
      HG = 4.800

37.95
4.80
     H.B. skin hollow
     wall entirely
     Phorpres Tuscan fcg
     bks laid stretcher
     bond in mor (1:1:6)
     + ptd wi neat w/s
     jt.

      EXTL 38.400   S.M.M. G9.
     angles
     4/0.275 = 1.100
    MEAN LENGTH 37.300

37.30
4.80
     Forming cavities 50mm
     wide in hollow walls
     incl 5 N. galv wire
     butterfly wall ties
     per m²

Ext. 38.400
Angles
4/2/0.275 2.200
Int. 36.200
angles
4/0.113 0.452
MEAN LENGTH 36.652

| 36.65 |
| 4.80 |

H.B. skin hollow
wall in c.b. laid
stretcher bond in
mor (1:1:6).

Int. 36.200
angles
4/0.225 0.900
MEAN LENGTH 37.100

| 37.10 |
| 0.23 |

One brk wall in c.b.
laid Eng bond
in ditto

PARTY
WALL
7.200
walls
2/0.275 0.550
L = 6.650

Ht = 4.800
0.225
5.025
6.650
2/0.225 0.450
L = 7.100

| 6.65 |
| 5.03 |
| ½/7.10 |
| 2.50 |

One brk wall
in c.b. ab.

2/0.450 = 0.900
0.563
L = 1.463

Scaled Ht = 2.550

Scaled 4.050
4.400
2) 8.450
Avg. 4.225

S.M.M. G3.4.5.

S.M.M. G3.4.5.
Centre-line of one brick wall does not
coincide with centre-line of cavity.

One brick wall measured over plate
without deduction - no bed plate to
be measured - S.M.M. G43.

S.M.M. G3.4.5.

5025

6650

Height from underside ceiling joist
to apex of brickwork scaled.

S.M.M. G3.4.5.

Height scaled to top of party wall.

63

2/1.46	
2.55	
2/0.45	
4.23	

Projections of chy breast 338 mm thk in ditto

Chimney breast & chimney stack measured as solid brickwork – no deduction for flues – S.M.M. G4.

$$
\begin{array}{r}
\text{Ht } 1.300 \\
1.000 \\
\hline
2)\,2.300 \\
\hline
\text{Avg. } 1.150
\end{array}
$$

S.M.M. G3.4.5.
Height measured from top of party wall

$$\frac{0.450}{0.225} = 2 \text{ Bks.}$$

0.90	
1.15	

Two lik chy stack in ditto

$$
\begin{array}{r}
0.900 \\
0.450 \\
\hline
2)\,1.350 \\
\hline
2.700
\end{array}
$$

S.M.M. G14.
Chimney stack.

2.70	
1.15	

E.O. cb for facewk in Prorpres Tuscan fcg bks laid Eng. bond & pld wi neat w/s jt.

(Fire opg
(& flue

opg 0.700
lintol 0.150
Ddt ————— 0.850

Fireplace openings and flue linings may be measured either with the walls or with Fires & Vents.

2/0.56	
0.85	

Proj of chy breast 338 mm thk ab.

Fire opening.
No deduction for ends of lintol –
S.M.M. G48.

$$
\begin{array}{r}
\text{ends } 0.563 \\
7/0.113 \;\; 0.226 \\
\hline
0.789
\end{array}
$$

S.M.M. F13.21.

2/ 1	

Precast conc (1:2:4) chamf. lintel size 789 x 112.5 x 150mm wi 2% wall hold ends, reinf wi & incl 1No 12mm dia m.s. bar, chamf face & soffit fin fair remainder keyed for plaster & bd. bdd in mor (1:1:6).

Scaled 5.500
0.900
0.500
0.500
―――――
7.400

2/ 7.40

200 mm dia fireclay flue lining to B.S. 1181 bedd & butt jtd in mor (1:1:6) incl cuttg to form easings and bends in lining & cuttg walls around lining

2

200 mm dia terra-cotta chimney pot to B.S. 1181 300mm high bedd & set in mor (1:1:6)

S.M.M. G55.

1

Precast conc (1:2:4) chy cap size 1000 × 550 × 75mm thk, throated all round, perforated for 2 No. 200 mm dia chy pots, fin fair on all exposed faces bedd & ptd in mortar (1:1:6).

S.M.M. F18.21.

S.M.M. G53.
Length scaled down centre-line of flue.

Plate 5
BRICK WALLS & CHIMNEY STACK

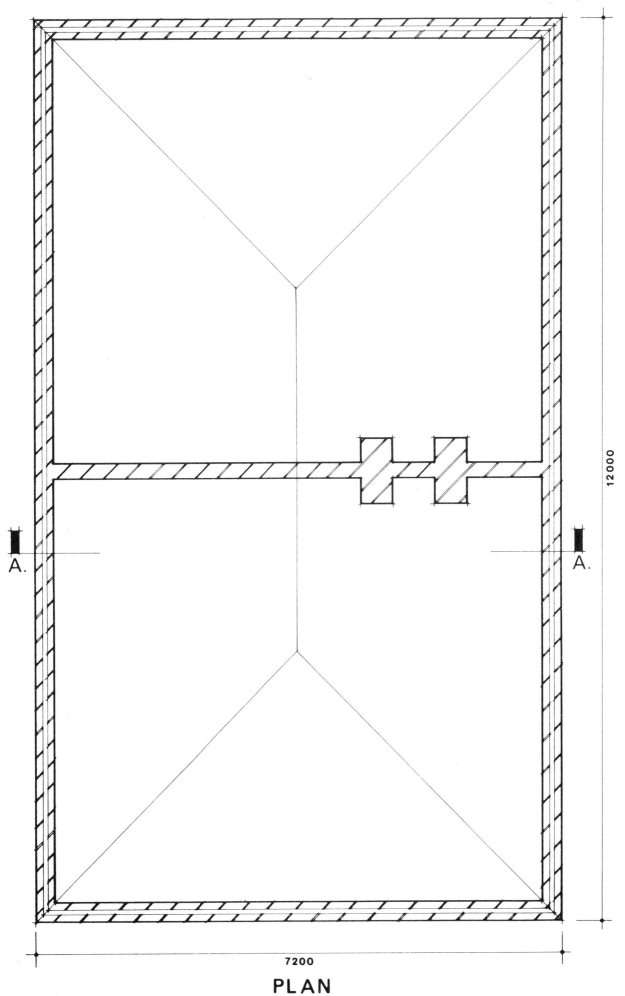

12000

7200

A.

A.

PLAN

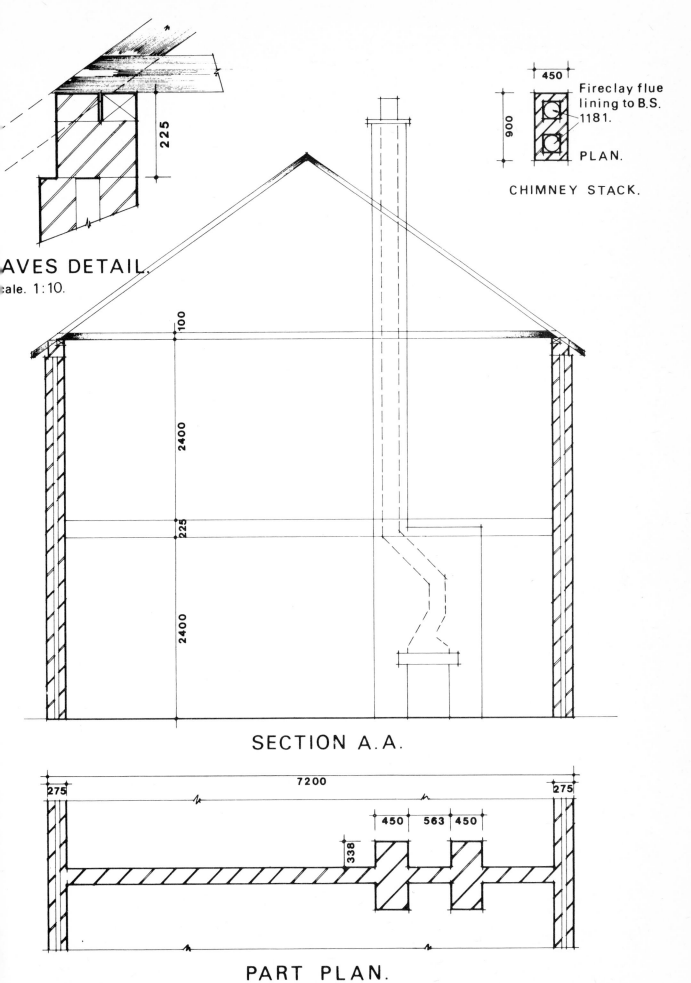

225

EAVES DETAIL.
Scale. 1:10.

450

900

Fireclay flue
lining to B.S.
1181.

PLAN.

CHIMNEY STACK.

100

2400

225

2400

SECTION A.A.

275   7200   275

450   563   450

338

PART PLAN.

Common Bricks laid Stretcher
or English Bond
Mortar (1 : 1 : 6).
"Phorpres" Tuscan Facing Bricks.

Scale. 1 : 50

Plate 6
BRICKWORK

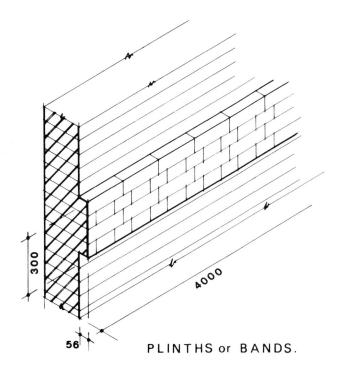

300

56

PLINTHS or BANDS.

4000

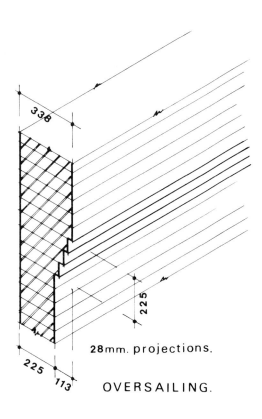

338

225

225

113

28mm. projections.

OVERSAILING.

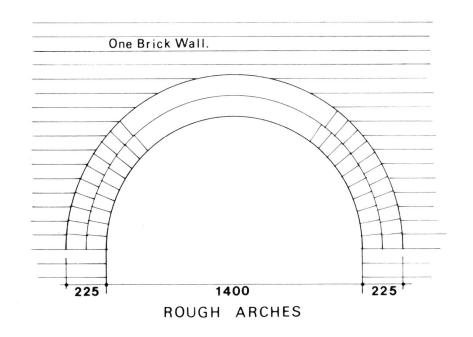

One Brick Wall.

225   1400   225

ROUGH ARCHES

Plate 6
BRICKWORK

PLINTH OR BAND COURSES

4·00		Projections 300 mm wide 56 mm deep in cb. laid Eng Bond in ct mor (1:3)	S.M.M. G5.10.

OVERSAILING.

338

225

225   28mm PROJECTS.

S.M.M. G5.10.

Bill diagram could be of value in this instance (S.M.M.A5.). (see example No. 10 – Trussed Rafter).

4.00		Projections 225 mm wide 56 mm Avg depth in cb laid Eng Bond in ct mor (1:3).

ROUGH ARCHES.

S.M.M. G12.

$$\frac{1·400}{2/\tfrac{1}{2}/0·225 \quad 0·225}$$
$$\overline{1·625}$$

½/3½/ 1·63	E.O. cb for rough arch 225 mm thk in two h.b. rings	

S.M.M. G57.

1	Centring to semi-circular bk arch 1400 mm span 225 mm wide on soffit

69

Plate 7
BRICK FACEWORK

SQUINT OR BIRDSMOUTH ANGLES.

1·00	Fair cutting birdsmouth angle &		<u>S.M.M. G15.</u>
	Fair purpose made squint angle in Pharpres Tuscan fcg bks.		<u>S.M.M. G15.</u>

SUNK BAND

4·00	E.O. cb for facewk a.d. to hog sunk band 225 mm wide set back 40 mm incl facewk to margins		<u>S.M.M. G16.</u> Facework as described refers to description of general facework which includes particulars of bricks, bond and pointing. Measure any ends and irregular angles if applicable.
4·00 0·23	<u>Ddt</u> E.O. cb. for facewk a.d.		General facework assumed previously measured.

70

PROJECTING BAND.

4.00	E.O. cb for facewk in type "B" fcg bks laid long band to hoz projecting plain band 225 mm wide set fwd 40 mm ptd wi neat w/s jt incl facewk to margins	S.M.M. G16. Assume that general facings are type "A" and the projecting band is in facings type "B". Facework type "B" differs from general facework, therefore description includes particulars of bricks, bond and pointing. Measure any ends and irregular angles if applicable.	
4.00 0.23	Ddt E.O. cb for facewk Type "A" a.d.	General facework.	

PROJECTING BRICK·ON·END BAND.

4.00	E.O. cb for facewk a.d. to hoz proj brick·on·end band 225 mm wide set fwd 40 mm incl facewk to margins	S.M.M. G17. Measure any ends and angles if applicable.	
4.00 0.23	Ddt E.O. cb for facewk a.d.	General facework.	

	SPLAYED PLINTH CAPPING	
4.00	E.O. cb. for facewk ad to hoz. stock pattern splayed plinth capping 75 mm wide entirely of headers set fwd 113 mm incl facewk to margins	S.M.M. G17.

Measure any ends and angles if applicable. |
| 4.00 / 0.08 | Ddt E.O. cb for facewk ad | General facework. |
| | ARCHES | |
| | 2/½/ 1.400
0.225 0.225
MEAN DIA: 1.625 | S.M.M. G20. |
| ½/3½/ 1.63 | E.O. cb for facewk ad. to semi circular arch 225 mm wide on face 100 mm wide on exposed soffit ＃
Ddt
E.O. cb for facewk ad   X 0.23 = | General facework.

S.M.M. G14. |
| | 2/½/ 1.625
0.225 0.225
EXT. DIA: 1.850 | |
| ½/3½/ 1.85 | Fair curved cuttg | |
| 1 | Centering to semi circular lik arch 1400 mm span 225 mm wide on soffit | S.M.M. G57. |

Plate 7
BRICK FACEWORK

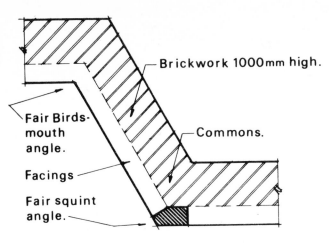

Brickwork 1000mm high.

Fair Birds-mouth angle.

Commons.

Facings

Fair squint angle.

SQUINT or BIRDS-MOUTH ANGLES.

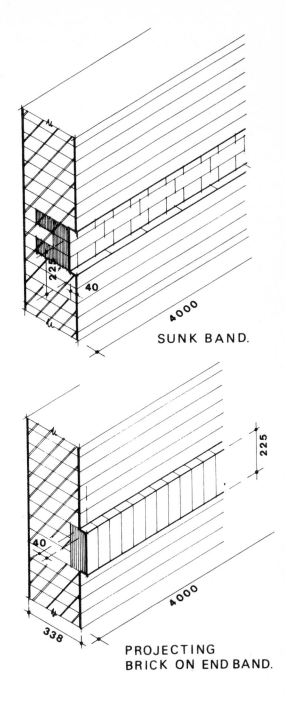

40

225

4000

SUNK BAND.

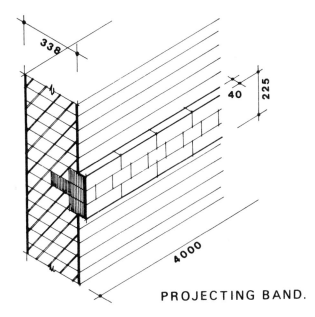

338

40

225

4000

PROJECTING BAND.

40

225

4000

338

PROJECTING
BRICK ON END BAND.

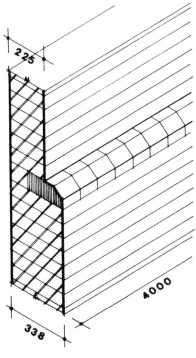

225

4000

338

SPLAYED PLINTH
CAPPING.

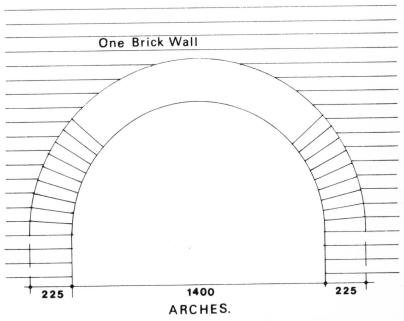

One Brick Wall

225

1400

225

ARCHES.

Plate 8
RUBBLE WALLING

<u>S.M.M. RULES</u>   SECTION A

         D.11.13.14.15.16.17.29.33.34.35.40.

         F.1.3.4.5.6.

         G.57.

         J.1.3.4.5.9.10.12.15.16.23.

<u>APPROACH:-</u>   Foundation trench

         Concrete foundation

         End piers

         Wall/attached piers/opening

         Reinstatement

2/0.200	0.400	<u>S.M.M. D11.13.</u>
2/0.600	1.200	
2/1.400	2.800	
2/0.500	1.000	
3/1.000	3.000	
L =	8.400	
Wall	0.400	
Spl 2/0.200	0.400	
W =	0.800	
	0.300	
	0.300	
D =	0.600	
End piers	0.600	
Spl 2/0.200	0.400	
	1.000	
Attached piers	0.500	
Spl 2/0.200	0.400	
	0.900	

PIER PROJECTIONS

8.400 TRENCH

1000   900

8.40	Exc tr to rec fdns	
0.80	stg G.L. max depth	
0.60	n.e. 1.00m	
2/2/ 1.00		
0.20	&	
0.60		
2/ 0.90	Filling to exc wi	<u>S.M.M. D33.34.35.</u>
0.20	matl arising from	
0.60	exc	
		<u>S.M.M. D11.15.16.17.</u>
2/ 8.40	Earthwork support	Twice times length X depth of trench
0.60	max depth n.e.	
2/ 1.20	1.00m & n.e. 2.00m	Ends of trench.
0.60	between opposing	
2/2/ 0.20	faces.	Pier returns.
0.60		

8.40	Level & compact	S.M.M. D40.
0.80	bot. exc	Length X width of trench.
2/1.00		
0.20		Pier projections.
2/0.90		
0.20		

8.40	Conc (1:2:4) fdns	S.M.M. F3.4.5.6.
0.80	in trenches	Length of trench X width and
0.30	150 – 300 mm thk	thickness of concrete.
2/1.00	poured agst.	
0.20	face of exc	Particulars of material given in
0.30	&	preamble in preference to description.
2/0.90		
0.20	Ddt.	
0.30	Filling to exc ab.	
	&	

Add
Remove exc matl
from site

S.M.M. D29.

(END
  PIERS

3.300
0.300
H = 3.600

S.M.M. J1.3.4.5.

Fair returns and flush pointing
measured to full height of rubble
work due to shallow depth of trench.

2/0.60	Hollington sandstone	
3.60	rough dressed	
	uncoursed random	
	rubble pier 800 mm	
	thk bedd jtd &	
	flush ptd both	
	sides in mor (1:1:6)	

WALL   PIER

S.M.M. J10.
For coping.

2/0.60	Levelling ditto 800mm	
	wide	
	&	

S.M.M. J15.
Measured as coping – no separate
provision for pier capping.

Hollington sandstone
ad. coping 800mm
wide avg. 300 mm
high bedd jtd &
ptd ab.

2/ 3.60	Fair return rubble work 800 mm wide	S.M.M. J12.	

WALL   PIER 800
200 → FAIR RETURNS

2/2/ 3.60	Ditto 200 mm wide

            (WALL

       2/1.400   2.800
       2/0.500   1.000
       3/1.000   3.000
          L =   6.800
     Scaled Ht.   3.300

S.M.M. J1.3.4.5.

Measured overall opening.

6.80 3.30	Hollington sandstone ad. wall 400 mm thk bdd jtd & ptd ab.

6.80	Levelling ditto 400 mm wide	S.M.M. J10. For coping.

&

Hollington sandstone ad. coping 400 mm wide avg 300 mm high ab.

S.M.M. J15.

          ATTACHED
          PIERS.
       Wall   0.400
       proj   0.200
       Pier   0.600

S.M.M. J1.3.4.5.

2/0.50 2.30	Hollington sandstone ad. pier 600 mm thk bdd jtd & ptd ab

&

WALL PIER WALL
FAIR RETURN

Ddt.
Ditto wall 400 mm thk ab.

2/2/ 2.30	Fair return rubble work 200 mm wide	S.M.M. J12.

1.00			
2.30			
7/ 0.50	Ddt		
0.50	Hollington sandstone ad. wall 400mm thk ab.		

2/ 2.30	Add	S.M.M. J12.	
	Fair return rubble work 400mm wide		
		S.M.M. J16.	

$$1.000$$
$$2/0.150 \quad 0.300$$
$$\text{MEAN DIA} = 1.300$$

3½/ 1.30	E.O. Hollington sandstone ad. wall 400 mm thk for semi-circular arch 300 mm wide on face 400 mm on soffit beld jtd & ptd ab.		

1	Centering to semi-circular rubble stone arch 1000mm span 400mm soffit	S.M.M. G57.	

(REINSTATE

$$\text{Wall } 6.800$$
$$\text{opg } 1.000$$
$$5.800$$

Volume of rubble work in the trench.

2/0.60	Ddt	End piers.	
0.80	Filling to exc ab		
0.30	&	Wall.	
5.80			
0.40	Add		
0.30	Remove exc	Attached piers.	
2/0.50	matl ab.		
0.20			
0.30			

77

Plate 8
RUBBLE WALLING

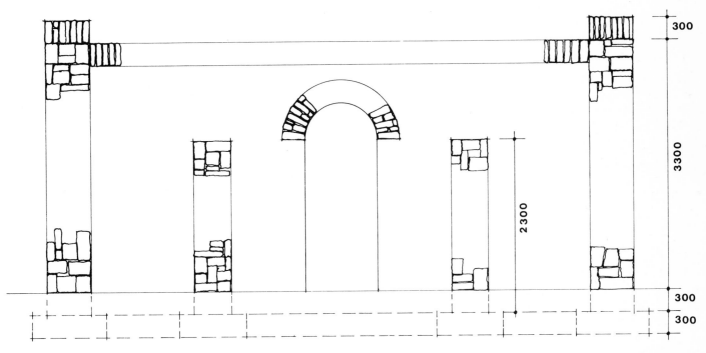

ELEVATION

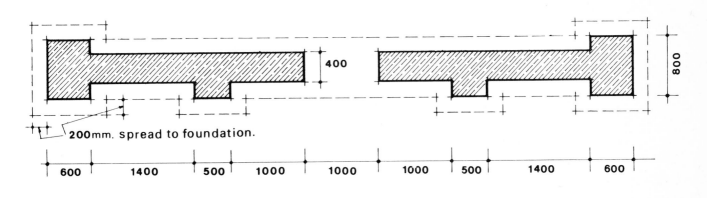

200mm. spread to foundation.

| 600 | 1400 | 500 | 1000 | 1000 | 1000 | 500 | 1400 | 600 |

PLAN

Concrete (1 : 2 : 4)
Hollington Sandstone, rough dressed, uncoursed random rubble,
bedded, jointed and flush pointed in mortar (1 : 1 : 6)

Scale. 1 : 50.

Chapter V

Roofs

Approach

(1) Divide large buildings into sections of manageable size. This is usually practicable in the case of flat roofs with expansion joints or similar well-defined divisions but is rarely so in the case of pitched roofs. Where a large project includes several buildings measure each as a separate unit.

(2) Measure individual roofs over all openings, recesses, projections and similar features which can be more easily dealt with by separate adjustment.

(3) Sub-divide each roof, irrespective of type, into:

    (a) Construction.

    (b) Coverings.

    (c) Eaves and rainwater installations.

    (d) Adjustments for openings, etc.

(4) The taker off must apply his knowledge of construction technology to determine the sequence of construction which, in most cases, will provide a logical sequence of measurement within the sub-sections listed above.

Measurement of roofs

A detailed plan of the roof should always be provided but where this is not done the dimensions of the roof must be calculated from those shown on the floor plans. It is then advantageous to prepare a roof plan, perhaps superimposed on the floor plan, and to carefully mark the gables, hips and valleys involved in pitched roofs and the rolls, drips and gutters involved in flat roofs.

TIMBER PITCHED ROOFS

Construction usually involves	plates purlins rafters, hip and valley rafters ridge ceiling joists and collars hangers, struts and beams roof trusses or trussed rafters
Coverings are usually	slate or tile roofing OR sheet roofing ALTHOUGH most other coverings may be employed
Eaves and rainwater installations include	eaves boarding fascia boards verge boarding barge boards rainwater gutters and fittings rainwater pipes and fittings

Roof shape. The shape of the roof on plan or the inclusion of hips and valleys has little effect upon the measurement of roofs where the pitch remains constant.

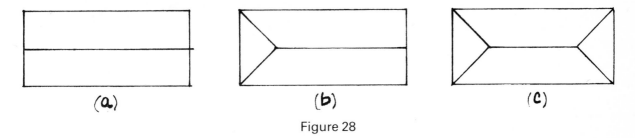

(a)   (b)   (c)

Figure 28

Roofs to rectangular buildings should each be measured as one complete unit.

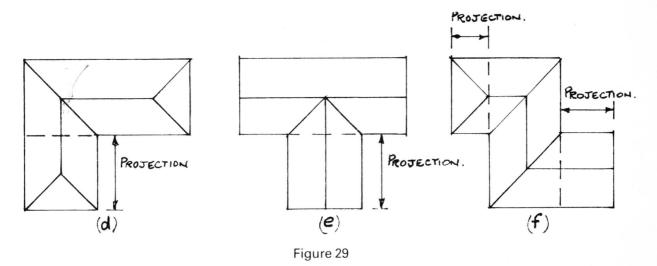

(d)   (e)   (f)

Figure 29

Roofs to more complicated buildings must be sub-divided into simple units, measuring the principal unit overall and adding the projections.

The inclusion of hips and valleys is ignored when measuring common rafters and no distinction is made between hipped and gabled roofs, since the total length of jack-rafters at a hip or valley is nominally equal to the length of the corresponding common rafters in a gable roof.

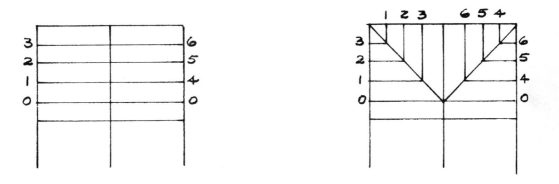

Figure 30

The combined length on plan of each pair of jack-rafters is equivalent to one common rafter.

The spacing of the rafters may not require a common rafter at the apex of the hip but this should always be measured since the length of the jack-rafters does not exactly equal the length of common rafters due to the splay cut ends.

The area of roof coverings is also unaffected by the inclusion of hips and valleys where the pitch remains constant.

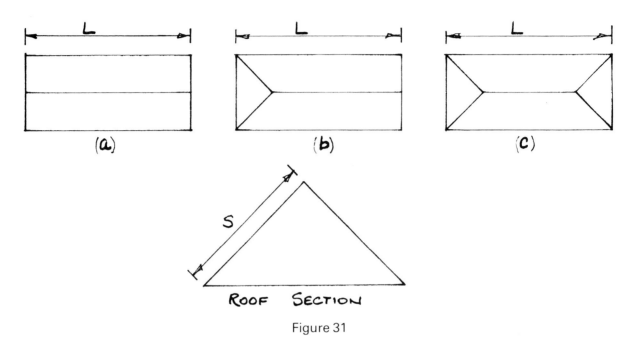

Figure 31

In each case the total roof area is twice times the overall length (L) multiplied by the roof slope (S).

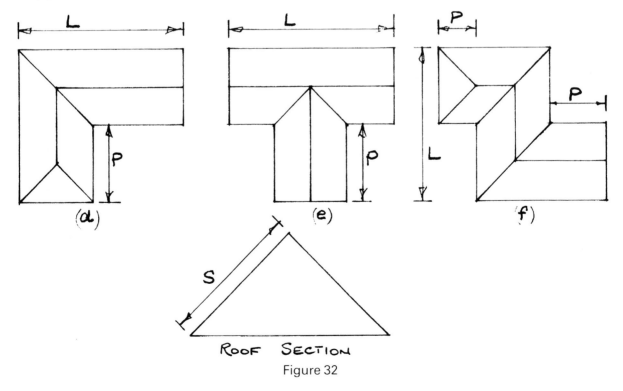

Figure 32

In each case the total area of the roof is twice times the overall length (L) multiplied by the roof slope (S) plus twice times the length (P) multiplied by the roof slope (S) for each projection.

At the intersection of roofs of different pitch it is essential to adjust the area of roof coverings.

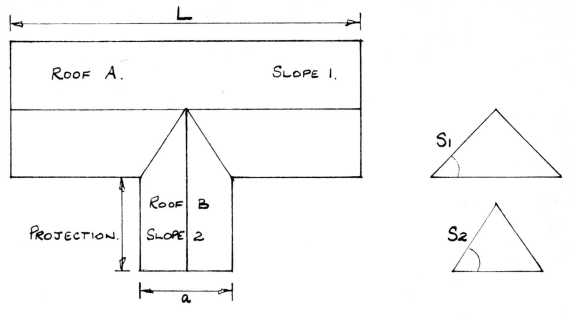

Figure 33

Area of roof A is twice times the overall length (L) multiplied by roof slope (S_1). Deduct from this area the area displaced at the roof intersection $\dfrac{a \times S_1}{2}$

Area of roof B is twice times the average length multiplied by the roof slope (S_2).

Gabled roof. The length of each common rafter may be determined by one of the following methods.

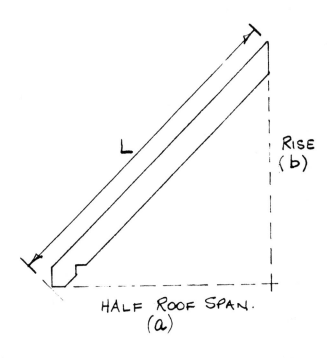

Figure 34

(1) Scale the length on slope direct from the drawing.

(2) Draw the roof outline on the dimension sheet to as large a scale as possible. Set out half the roof span along the bottom edge of the sheet and the rise on the vertical edge. Scale off the hypotenuse to give length of rafter.

(3) Use Pythagoras' theorem. $L = \sqrt{a^2 + b^2}$

(4) Use trigonometry. $L = a \times \sec 45°$.

In practice scaling the dimensions as described in methods (1) and (2) is sufficiently accurate.

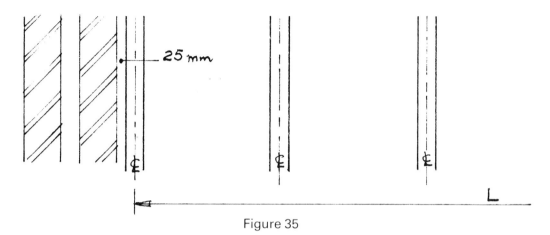

Figure 35

The number of common rafters may be calculated as follows:

(1) Find length between gable walls.

(2) Deduct 25 mm clearance at each wall.

(3) Deduct half of rafter width at each wall to give the length centre to centre, between first and last rafters.

(4) Divide by centre-line spacing of rafters to give number of spaces.

(5) Add one to give number of rafters required on each roof slope.

(6) Should this calculation not produce an exact number of spaces decide either to increase slightly the spacing of rafters or to add an extra rafter. In most cases it is advisable to add an extra rafter.

(7) Twice times the number of rafters calculated to provide for both sides of the roof.

Hipped roof. The length of each common rafter is determined by one of the four methods previously described for a gabled roof.

The number of common rafters may be calculated as follows:

(1) Find overall length of roof.

(2) Divide by centre-line spacing of rafters to give number of spaces.

(3) Add one to give total number of rafters required in the length of the roof.

(4) Should this calculation not produce an exact number of spaces decide either to increase slightly the spacing of rafters or to add an extra rafter. In most cases it is advisable to add an extra rafter.

(5) Calculate the number of common rafters by deducting from the total number any hip or valley rafters since these are of different dimensions and measured separately.

(6) Twice times the number of common rafters calculated to provide for both sides of roof.

(7) Add one apex rafter for each hipped end.

The length of a hip or valley rafter cannot be scaled direct from the roof plan since the length required is the length on slope. The length is clearly the hypotenuse of a triangle, the base of which is the horizontal length of the hip or valley on plan and the height the rise of the roof. One of the following methods must therefore be adopted:

(1)

Figure 36

Set off on the roof plan a line at right angles to one of the hips and mark off a length equal to the rise of the roof. The hypotenuse so formed is the length of the hip. Method (a) is suitable only where the roof pitch remains constant.

(2)   Draw the roof outline on the dimension sheet to as large a scale as possible. Set out the hip length on plan along the bottom edge of the sheet and the rise of the roof on the vertical edge. Scale off hypotenuse to give length of hip or valley.

(3)   Use Pythagoras' theorem.

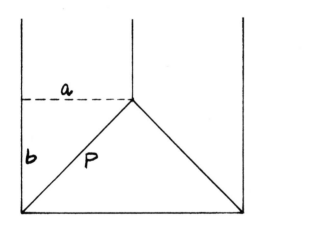 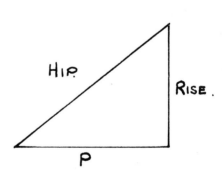

Figure 37

Find plan length of hip (P).

$P = \sqrt{a^2 + b^2}$ a = half roof span
                                 b = half roof span only where roof pitch remains constant

Hip length = $\sqrt{p^2 + r^2}$ r = rise of roof

In practice scaling the dimensions as described in methods (1) and (2) is sufficiently accurate.

85

TIMBER FLAT ROOFS

Construction usually involves	plates and beams joists and firrings strutting roof boarding and base boarding gutter boarding drips and rolls as required
Coverings are usually	bitumen-felt roofing sheet metal roofing
Eaves and rainwater installation	eaves boarding fascia boards rainwater gutters and fittings rainwater pipes and fittings

Calculation of joists required.

(1) Find length of roof between walls.

(2) Deduct 25 mm clearance at each wall.

(3) Deduct half of joists width at each wall to give the length, centre to centre, between first and last joists.

(4) Divide by spacing of joists to find number of spaces.

(5) Add one to give number of joists required.

(6) Should this calculation not produce an exact number of spaces decide either to increase slightly the spacing of joists or to add and extra joist. In most cases it is advisable to add an extra joist.

Where short joists are required to provide an eaves projection the number of such joists should be calculated in similar manner.

Strutting. This is rarely shown on the drawings but must be measured where necessary.

INSITU CONCRETE FLAT ROOFS

Construction usually involves	concrete formwork reinforcement beams
Coverings include	asphalt bitumen-felt roofing insitu-finishings tile, slab or block finishings

MESSRS X.Y. & PARTNERS.

Metric
Bar Schedule   ref.   ☐☐☐ ☐☐ ☐

Date.

Site Ref.

Member.	Bar mark	Type and size	No. of mbrs	No. in each	Total No.	Length of each bar mm	Shape code	A mm	B mm	C mm	D mm	E/r mm

Figure 38

Bar reinforcement schedules. The preferred form of schedule recommended by BS 4466 'Bending dimensions and scheduling of bars for the reinforcement of concrete', is illustrated in Figure 38 (page 86).

Bending dimensions. The minimum allowances for hooks, bends, stirrups and links for mild steel bars to BS 4449 are as follows:

semi-circular hooks

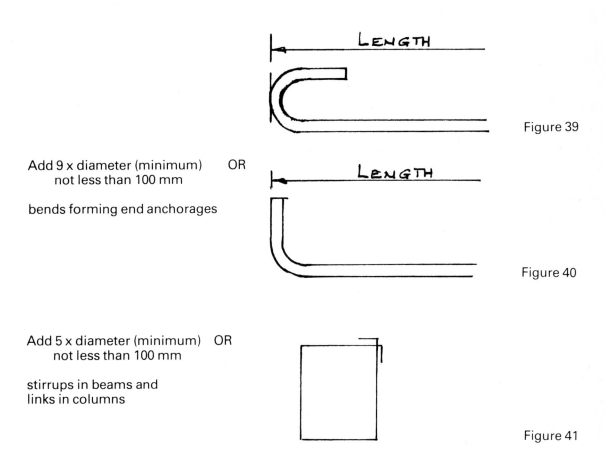

Figure 39

Add 9 x diameter (minimum)   OR
     not less than 100 mm

bends forming end anchorages

Figure 40

Add 5 x diameter (minimum)   OR
     not less than 100 mm

stirrups in beams and
links in columns

Figure 41

Length = internal girth + 20 x diameter of bar

STEEL BEAMS. Unfabricated steelwork, such as that often involved in flat roofs, must be given under an appropriate heading for each different building or independant structure (SMM P3).

The unit of billing for structural steelwork is the tonne. Beams are measured linear and the weight per linear metre is indicated below the description of each member so that the worker up may calculate the total weight of the item.

TIMBER FRAMEWORK. Where a steel beam projects below the ceiling, any timber framework required to support the finishings to the sides and soffit of the steel beam is measured with the internal finishings group.

Plate 9
PITCHED ROOF

<u>S.M.M. RULES</u>

SECTION A.
    G.43.
    M.1.3.4.5.6.9.10.11.13.16.17.
    N.1.2.3.4.5.11.30.
    R.1.3.4.5.6.7.8.9.10.
    V.1.2.3.4.

<u>APPROACH:-</u>

Construction – plates
    common rafters
    hip & valley rafters
    ridge
    ceiling joists
    insulating quilts

The sequence of measurement follows closely the order of construction.

Coverings   – tile roofing
    underlay
    eaves
    verge
    hips & valley
    ridge

Eaves &
rainwater
installation – eaves boarding
    fascia board
    rainwater gutter & fittings
    rainwater pipe & fittings

Adjustments – Refer to separate examples –
    Adjustments for chimney stack

(Construction

Bldg overall 10.000
walls 2/0.275 0.550
         9.450 –

Bldg 9/a 7.500
Walls 0.550 6.950 –
    2/ 16.400
    INTL = 32.800
Gable 4.500
Walls 0.550 3.950
    28.850

Halving
at Hips 3/2/0.100 0.600 –
Halved
joints 4/0.150 = 0.600
    30.050
    10.000
    4.500
    5.500 –

30.05

100 x 75 mm Sawn
S.w. pitched roofs

S.M.M. N1.3.
For measurement of labours, ends, angles, mitres, intersections etc.

over 4.20 metres long – S.M.M. N1.

over 4.20 metres long – S.M.M. N1.

halving at valley already included.

for lengths over 4.20 metres.

over 4.20 metres long – S.M.M. N1.
S.M.M. N1.
plate
particulars of quality given in
Preamble in preference to description

		28.850		Internal angle cancels out one external angle.

Angles 2/0.100 0.200
———————
29.050 — Centre line of plate.

| 29.05 | | Bed plate 100 mm wide in mor (1:1:6) | — · · | S.M.M. G43. Brickwork assumed measured to underside of plate. |

      L. Scales 2.980   S.M.M. N1.2.

Bldg o/a = 10.000
Eaves
O'hang 2/0.175 = 0.350
————
Roof o/a 10.350

$\dfrac{10350}{400}$ = 25+1+1 = 27

less hip/valley   2
Common Rafters = 25

      7.500
      4.500
————
Projection   3.000
Verge 0.050
gable 0.275
clearance 0.025
& rafter 0.025   0.375
————
2.625

$\dfrac{2625}{400}$ = 6+1+1 = 8

less valley $\dfrac{1}{7}$

2/ 25/ 2.98		50 × 100 mm sawn s.w. pitched roofs	—	rafters
2.98				
2/7/ 2.98				

      L. Scales 3.900   S.M.M. N1.2.

| 4/ 3.90 | | 50 × 150 mm ditto | — | hip and valley rafters |

89

Bldg 4.500

Eaves
O'hang $\frac{2}{}$/0.175 0.350

Span 4.850

Roof $\%_a$ 10.350

$2/\frac{1}{2}/4.850$ 4.850
    5.500

Scarf jt $\frac{2}{}$/0.150 0.300 — over 4.20 meters long — S.M.M. N1.

  L = 5.800

 Bldg 7.500
 eaves 0.175
    7.675

wall cavity 0.050
lk skin 0.113 = 0.163
    7.512

$\frac{1}{2}$/4.850 2.425

  L = 5.087 — over 4.20 meters long — S.M.M. N1.

Scarf jt 0.300
  L = 5.387

5.80
5.39

25 × 150 mm ditto — ridges

L Scaled = 4.460
INTL = 9.450

Clearance
$\frac{2}{}$/0.025 = 0.050
£ joists
$\frac{2}{}$/0.025 = 0.050 = 0.100
    9.350

$\dfrac{9350}{400} = 23 + 1 + 1 = \underline{25}$

 Clg jsts 4.460
4.500
Walls
$\frac{2}{}$/0.275 0.550 3.950
   2) 0.510

  Proj = 0.255
Projection 3.000
Clg jsts 0.255
Clearance 0.025
£ jsts
0.025
0.038 0.063 = 0.343
    2.654

90

50×100 mm

50×100 mm CLG JOISTS

CLG JOISTS

PLATE

75×175 mm CLG JOIST

50×100 mm

$$\frac{2657}{400} = 6+1+1 = 8$$

less trimmer $\dfrac{1}{7}$

25/ 7/	4·46	50 × 100 mm ditto	– ceiling joists
	4·46	75 × 175 mm ditto	– support to ends of ceiling joists across roof intersection. S.M.M. N30.

INTL	9·450
plate 2/0·100	0·200
L =	9·650
INTL	3·950
	0·200
	4·150
	7·500
	4·500
	3·000
gable	0·100
	2·900

– measured to back of plate

	9·65 4·15	75 mm thk fibreglass insulating quilt wi 150 mm laps laid loose over jsts.	
	4·15 2·90		

S.M.M. M.3.4.5.6.16.

(Coverings

Bldg 9/a	10·000
Eaves O'hang	
2/0·250	0·500
	10·500
	7·500
	4·500
	3·000
less eaves O'hang	0·250
	2·750
Verge O'hang	0·050
	2·800

2/	10·50 2·98	380 × 230 mm conc interlockg tile roofg to 75 mm lap, 35° pitch, each tile nailed every alternate cos wi one aluminium alloy nail on & incl 38 × 19 mm sawn s.w. battens	Particulars of quality given in Preamble in preference to description
2/	2·80 2·98		

91

2/ 10.50 2.98 2/ 2.80 2.98	Underlay of reinf bituminous felt lapped 150 mm @ jts & nailed to bdg. wi galv clout nails		S.M.M. M17.
			S.M.M. M8. Double course at eaves not require[d] with this type of tile roofing.
2.98	E.O. tile roofg for verge incl extra undercloak cos in plain tiles b.+p. in ct mor (1:3) & Ditto wi purpose made left hand verge tile incl ditto	– –	S.M.M. M9. R.H. verge Left hand verge requires purpose made tile – see detail.
3/ 3.90	E.O. tile roofg for third round hip capping to match main tiling b+p in ct mor (1:3)		S.M.M. M11.
2/3/ 3.90	cuttg tile roofg to hips subsequently covered. &		S.M.M. M11.
	Rakg cuttg bit. felt underlay		S.M.M. M17.
2	mitred intersection ridge & hip capping		S.M.M. M11.
3	Filled end in ct mor (1:3) &		S.M.M. M11.
92	Galv. iron hip iron scrd to bdg.		S.M.M. M13.

3.90	E.O. tile roofg for purpose made valley tiles	S.M.M. 110. see separate detail.		
2/3.90	Cuttg tile roofg to valleys incl b+p in ct mor (1:3)	S.M.M. M10.		
	& Rakg cuttg felt underlay	S.M.M. M17.		
5.50 5.30	E.O. tile roofg for half round ridge cappg to match main tiling b.+p. in ct mor (1:3)	S.M.M. M1. Intersection already measured with hips.		
1	Filled end in ct mor (1:3)	S.M.M. M1.		
	(Eaves & R.W Installation	S.M.M. N1.4.		

$$\begin{array}{rr} & 0.200 \\ \text{fascia} & 0.025 \\ \hline & 0.175 \\ \text{groove} & 0.010 \\ \hline W = & 0.185 \\ \text{Bldg o/a} = & 10.000 \\ & 7.500 \\ \hline 2/ & 17.500 \\ \hline & 35.000 \\ \text{less gable} & 4.500 \\ \hline & 30.500 \\ \text{Extn angles} & \\ 3/2/0.185 = & 1.110 \\ \hline L = & 31.610 \end{array}$$

31.61	185 x 19 mm West S.w. t.&g. eaves bdg	S.M.M. N4. 19 X 185 mm = 0.0034 m^2		
2/ 1	End ditto	S.M.M. N1.		93
4	Angles ditto	S.M.M. N1.		

30·50	25 × 50 mm sawn s.w. ground plugged to bkk		S.M.M. N11.

	30·500
²/₀.₂₀₀	0·800
	31·300

31·30	25 × 150 mm wrot s.w. grooved fascia bd.

25 X 150 mm = 0.0038 m²

2	Ends	S.M.M. N1.
4	mitres	S.M.M. N1.

²/ 1   19 mm Ikk wrot s.w. spandril boxed end size 200 × 240 mm tall

No express provision for this item in S.M.M.

boxed end to eaves

	30·500
²/₀.₁₇₅	0·350
	30·850

S.M.M. V1.2.3.4.
S.M.M. V3 — measured in square meters — not isolated surfaces.

30·85	K.P.S. ③
0·18	General wood surfs Ex'n.
31·30	
0·20	
²/0·20	
0·24	

150   175   25

S.M.M. R1.3.4.5.6.7.8.

	fascia	31·300
proj ²/₀.₁₀₀		0·200
		31·500
Verge ²/₀.₀₇₅		0·150
		31·650

94

31·65	100 mm dia extl P.V.C. H.R. socketted eaves gutter jtd wi gutter straps & union clips fxd wi P.V.C. bkts scrd to s.w. @ 900 mm ⁰/c incl jts in running length			
4	E.O. angles	S.M.M. R7.		
2	E.O. stop end & E.O. outlet wi nozzle for 75 mm dia pipe	S.M.M. R7. S.M.M. R7.		
2/3·00	75 mm dia extl P.V.C. rainwater pipe wi socketted jts fxd wi P.V.C. socket pipe clips p.& s. to faced bkk @ 1000 mm ⁰/c incl jts in running length	S.M.M. R9.10. Pipes measured overall pipe fittings.		
2	E.O. swanneck 200 mm proj & E.O. shoe	S.M.M. R10. S.M.M. R10.		

assumed length 3.00m

95

Plate 9
PITCHED ROOF

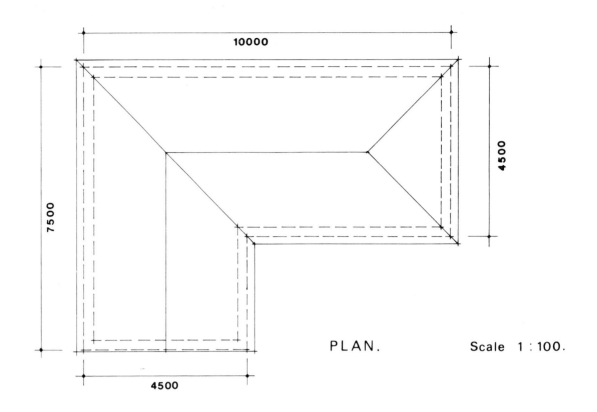

PLAN.   Scale 1 : 100.

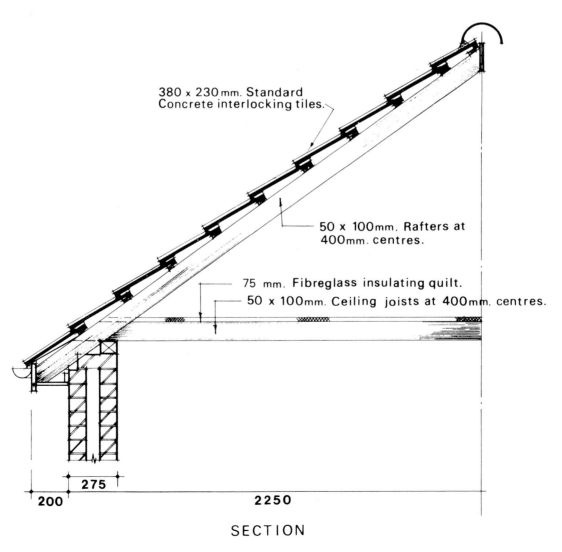

380 x 230 mm. Standard
Concrete interlocking tiles.

50 x 100mm. Rafters at
400mm. centres.

75 mm. Fibreglass insulating quilt.

50 x 100mm. Ceiling joists at 400mm. centres.

SECTION

Scale 1 : 20.

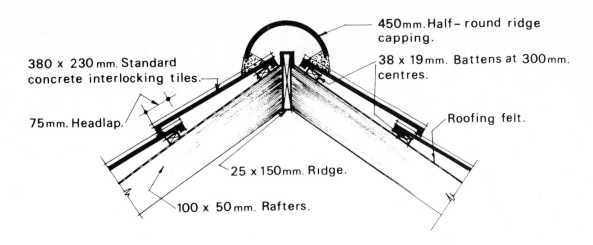

450mm. Half-round ridge capping.

380 x 230 mm. Standard concrete interlocking tiles.

38 x 19mm. Battens at 300mm. centres.

75mm. Headlap.

Roofing felt.

25 x 150mm. Ridge.

100 x 50mm. Rafters.

SECTION THROUGH RIDGE.

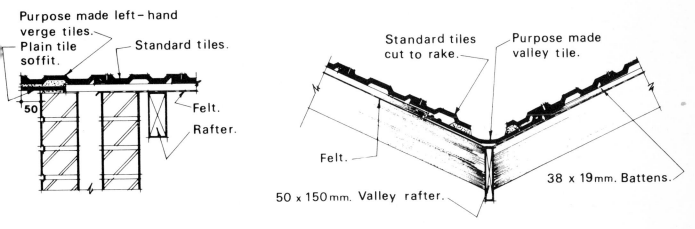

Purpose made left-hand verge tiles.

Plain tile soffit.

Standard tiles.

50

Felt.

Rafter.

SECTION THROUGH VERGE.

Standard tiles cut to rake.

Purpose made valley tile.

Felt.

50 x 150mm. Valley rafter.

38 x 19mm. Battens.

SECTION THROUGH VALLEY.

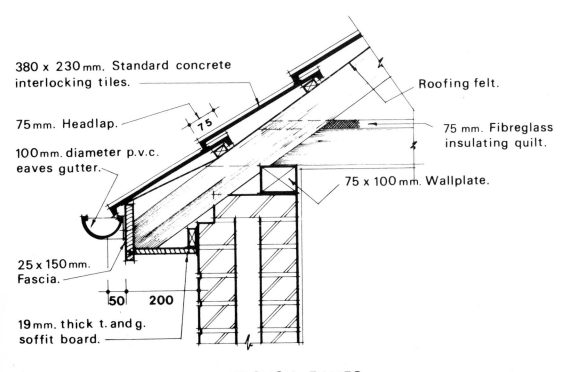

380 x 230mm. Standard concrete interlocking tiles.

75mm. Headlap.

75

100mm. diameter p.v.c. eaves gutter.

Roofing felt.

75 mm. Fibreglass insulating quilt.

75 x 100 mm. Wallplate.

25 x 150mm. Fascia.

50   200

19mm. thick t. and g. soffit board.

SECTION THROUGH EAVES.

Scale 1 : 10.

Plate 10
TRUSSED RAFTER

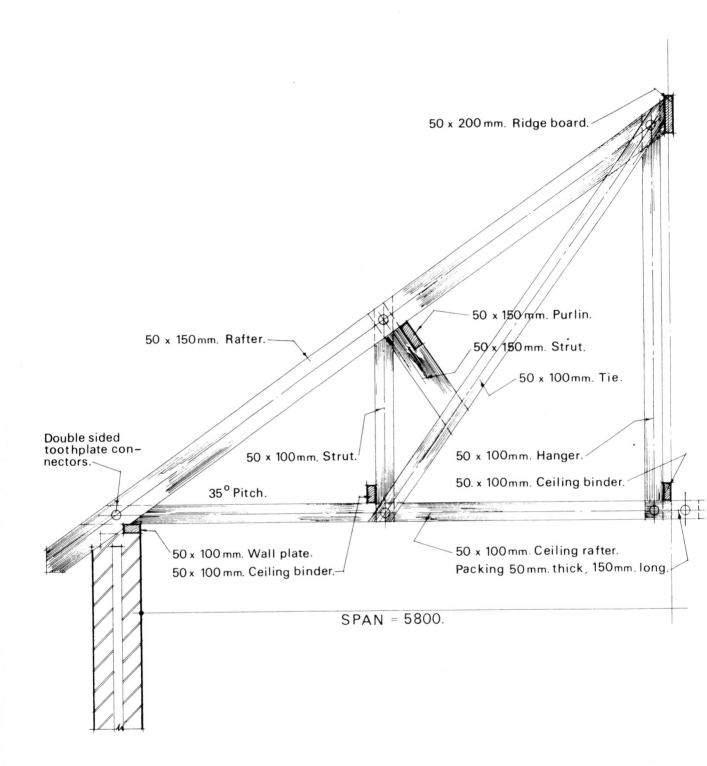

50 x 200 mm. Ridge board.

50 x 150 mm. Rafter.

50 x 150 mm. Purlin.

50 x 150 mm. Strut.

50 x 100 mm. Tie.

Double sided toothplate connectors.

50 x 100 mm. Strut.

50 x 100 mm. Hanger.

50. x 100 mm. Ceiling binder.

35° Pitch.

50 x 100 mm. Wall plate.

50 x 100 mm. Ceiling binder.

50 x 100 mm. Ceiling rafter.

Packing 50 mm. thick, 150 mm. long.

SPAN = 5800.

HALF ELEVATION.   Scale. 1 : 20.

⊕ 50 mm. dia. double sided, toothed plate connectors, with 13 mm. dia. bolts. Each bolt with 50 mm. square, 3 mm. thick mild steel washer under head and nut.

Plate 10
TRUSSED RAFTER

S.M.M. RULES

APPROACH:-

SECTION A
        N.1.17.18.

Emmerate separately each type of
trussed rafter. Bill diagrams must
be used unless they can be adequately
described.

S.M.M. N1.17.18.

S.M.M. A5 - Bill diagrams:-
These are normally single line
drawings provided by the quantity
surveyor.   They can be included
in the description or as a separate
facing page. They can also be
bound together as an appendix at the
back of the bills - if this method
is used, each diagram and description
should be given a reference number.

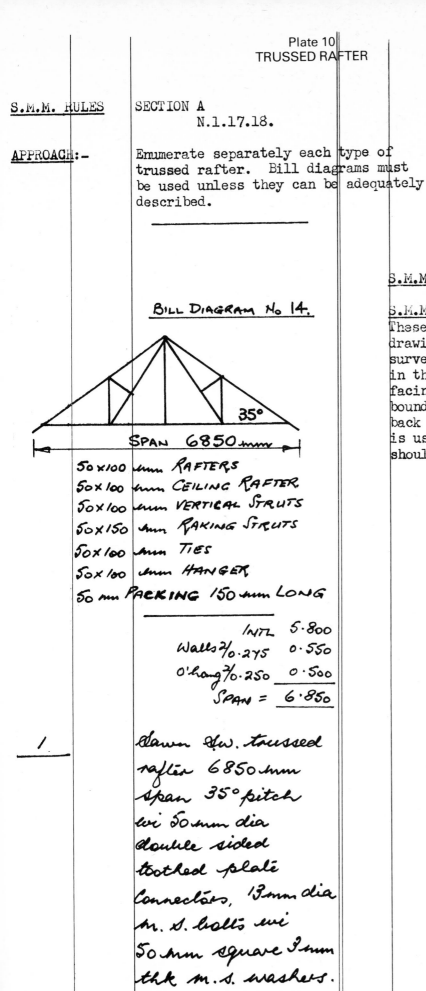

BILL DIAGRAM No 14.

35°

SPAN 6850 mm

50 x 100 mm RAFTERS
50 x 100 mm CEILING RAFTER
50 x 100 mm VERTICAL STRUTS
50 x 150 mm RAKING STRUTS
50 x 100 mm TIES
50 x 100 mm HANGER
50 mm PACKING 150 mm LONG

INTL	5.800
Walls 2/0.275	0.550
O'hang 2/0.250	0.500
SPAN =	6.850

1

Sawn s.w. trussed
rafter 6850 mm
span 35° pitch
wi 50 mm dia
double sided
toothed plate
connectors, 13mm dia
m.s. bolts wi
50 mm square 3mm
thk m.s. washers.

(Bill diagram No 14)

Plate 11
CHIMNEY STACK 'A'

S.M.M. RULES.	SECTION A

G.47.
M.4.6.7.17.48.49.50.53.
N.1.2.3.4.10.

APPROACH:-   Construction – common rafters

Coverings   – tile roofing
underlay

Flashings   – apron
stepped flashing
gutter
flashing.

Adjust the Construction and Coverings in the sequence used for the measurement of the Roof.

(Adjustment
(Stack "A"

stack   1·013

clearance
2/0·025 = 0·050

± Rafters
2/0·025 = 0·050 0·100
_____
1·113

$\frac{1113}{400}$ = 2+1+1 = 4

less trimming   2
_____
trimmed = 2

S.M.M. N1.2.

Common rafters as measured previously in hipped roof – to be replaced by 75mm thick trimming rafters.

50mm RAFTERS REPLACED WITH 75mm TRIMMINGS

50mm RAFTERS TRIMMED

2/ 2.98	] Ddt-	–	common rafters
2/0·96	50 × 100 mm sawn	–	common rafters trimmed. (scaled).
	s.w. pitched roofs		

stack   1·013
clearance   0·050
trimming 2/0·075   0·150
tusk 2/2/3/0·100   0·133
_____
1·346

tusk = $\frac{2}{3}$ depth of rafter.

| 2/ 2.98 |] Add | – | trimming rafters |
| 2/ 1.35 | 75 × 100 mm ditto | – | trimmers |

100

		slack 1·013 clearance 0·050 1·063	S.M.M. N3.		
1		Trimming 50 × 100 mm ditto around opg size 1063 × 960 mm			
1·01 1·14		Ddt 380 × 230 mm conc tile roofg a.b. &	S.M.M. M4.6.		
		Ddt Bitumen felt underlay a.b.	S.M.M. M17.		
1·01 2/1·14		Square cuttg tile roofg arnd opg.	S.M.M. M7. S.M.M. M8. Double course at eaves not required with this type of tile roofing		
1·01		50 × 38 mm sawn s.w. splayed tilting fillet	S.M.M. N10.		
		ends ²/0·150 1·013 0·300 1·313	S.M.M. M48.49.50.		
1·31		milled lead Code No 5. B.S.1178 apron 300 mm gth wi lead clips & tacks & 100 mm intermediate laps all lead wedged into groove and dressing over interlocking tiles across the corrugations &			
		Rake out hoz jt in bkk for turned in edge of flashing & jt in mor (1:1:6).	S.M.M. G47.		

$$\begin{array}{r} 0.840 \\ \text{ends } \%0.100 \quad \underline{0.200} \\ \underline{1.040} \end{array}$$

2/1·04

milled lead a.b. stepped flashing 300 mm gth wi clips, tacks & laps a.b. lead wedged into groove & dressing over interlocking tiles along the corrugations

&

S.M.M. G.47.

Rake out stepped jt in bkk for turned in edge of flashing a.b.

$$\begin{array}{r} \text{stack } 1·013 \\ \text{ends } \%0.150 \quad \underline{0.300} \\ \underline{1·313} \end{array}$$

S.M.M. M.48.49.53.

$$\begin{array}{r} \text{upstand } 0·150 \\ \text{gutter } 0·150 \\ \text{slope } \underline{0·300} \\ \underline{0·600} \end{array}$$

1·31

milled lead a.b. lining to sloping gutter 600 mm gth wi clips, tacks & laps a.b. lead wedged into groove, dressed over tilting fillet and up roof slope

2/1

Bossed end

S.M.M. M.53.

1·01		25 mm Thk wrot Jw. butt jtd Gutter side 300 mm wide	S.M.M. M.4.	

25 mm Thk wrot
Jw. butt jtd
Gutter side 300 mm
wide

&

25 mm Thk wrot
Jw. gutter bdg.
150 mm wide

2/ 1   Gusset end.   S.M.M. M.

          Stack 1·013
ends %·100 0·200
              1·213   S.M.M. M48,49,50.

1·21   milled lead a.b.
flashg 150 mm gth
wi clips, tacks
& laps a.b. lead
wedged into groove.

&

Rake out hoz jt
in bkk for
turned in edge
flashg a.b.   S.M.M. G47.

Plate 11
CHIMNEY STACK 'B'

S.M.M. RULES.

SECTION A
     G.47.
     M.4.6.7.11.14.17.48.49.50.54.55.
     N.1.2.3.

APPROACH:-

Construction - common rafters
                 ridge

Coverings   - tile roofing
                 underlay

Flashings   - aprons
                 stepped flashing
                 soakers
                 saddle

Adjust the Construction and Coverings in the sequence used for the measurement of the Roof.

(Adjustment
   stack "B"

stack 0.675

S.M.M. N1.2.
Common rafters as measured previously in hipped roof to be replaced by 75mm thick trimming rafters.

clearance
$^2/0.025 = 0.050$
& rafters
$^2/0.025 = 0.050$ 0.100
$\overline{0.775}$

$\dfrac{775}{400} = 1+1+1 = 3$

less trimming $\underline{2}$

trimmed on each $\underline{1}$
     slope

$^2/_2$ 2.98	Ddt	—	common rafters
$^2/$ 0.68	50 × 100 mm sawn	—	common rafters trimmed (scaled).
	s.w. pitched roofs		

stack   0.675
clearance   0.050
trimming $^2/0.075$ 0.150
tusk $^2/\frac{2}{3}/0.100$ 0.133
$\overline{1.008}$

— tusk = $\frac{2}{3}$ depth of rafter

$^2/_2$ 2.98	Add	—	trimming rafters
$^2/$ 1.01	75 × 100 mm ditto	—	trimmers

	stack 0.675			
	clearance 0.050			
	0.725			
0.73	Ddt:	–	ridge	
	50 × 150 mm ditto			
	stack 1.013		S.M.M. N3.	
	clearance 0.050		Size of stack on plan	
	1.063			
1	Trimming 50 × 100 mm			
	ditto around opg			
	size 1063 × 725 mm			
2/0.68	Ddt		S.M.M. M4.6.	
0.60	265 × 165 plain			
	conc tile roofg			
	a.b.			
	&			
	Ddt			
	Bitumen felt		S.M.M. M17.	
	underlay a.b.			
2/0.68	Square cuttg		S.M.M. M7.	
2/0.60	tile roofg			
	arnd opg.			
0.68	Ddt		S.M.M. M11.	
	E.O. half round			
	ridge cappg a.b.			

				0.675	S.M.M. M48.49.50.
			ends 2/0.150	0.300	
				0.975	

2/ 0.98

milled lead Code
No 5. B.S. 1178
apron 300 mm grth
wi lead clips &
tacks & 100 mm
intermediate laps
all lead wedged
into groove

&

Rake out hoz. jt.
in bkk for
turned in edge
flashg & pt. in
mor (1:1:6)

S.M.M. G47.

	0.600	S.M.M. M48.49.50.
end	0.100	
	0.700	

2/2/ 0.70

milled lead a.b.
stepped flashg
175 mm grth wi
clips, tacks &
laps a.b.

2/2/ 0.60

Rake out stepped
jt in bkk for
turned in edge
of flashg a.b.

S.M.M. G47.

/6	6			

Supply
milled lead Code
No 3. B.S. 1178
cloaker size
190 × 175 mm and
hand to tiler

&

Fix ditto by
tiler

. . .

milled lead Code
No 5. B.S. 1178
saddle size
320 × 550 mm
overall, incl
dressing & lossing
at ridge abutment.

2/	1

S.M.M. M54.

LENGTH = Gauge + Lap + 25mm =
 100 + 65 + 25   = 190mm

WIDTH = 75 └─── = 175mm
                100

NUMBER = Slope = 600 = 6 on each
          Gauge   100   slope

S.M.M. M14.

S.M.M. M55.

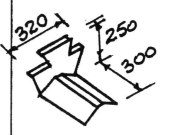

Plate 11
CHIMNEY STACK 'A'

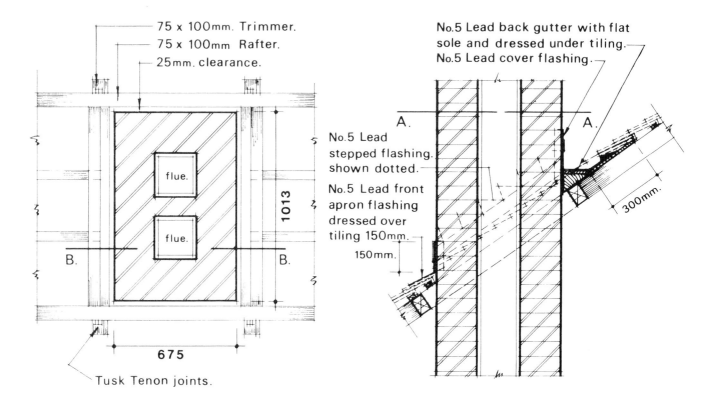

75 x 100mm. Trimmer.
75 x 100mm Rafter.
25mm. clearance.

flue.

flue.

1013

B. B.

675

Tusk Tenon joints.

No.5 Lead back gutter with flat sole and dressed under tiling.
No.5 Lead cover flashing.

A. A.

No.5 Lead stepped flashing. shown dotted.

No.5 Lead front apron flashing dressed over tiling 150mm.

150mm.

300mm.

PLAN OF CHIMNEY AT A.A.

SECTION THROUGH STACK AT B.B.

CHIMNEY STACK 'B'

Scale.   1 : 20.

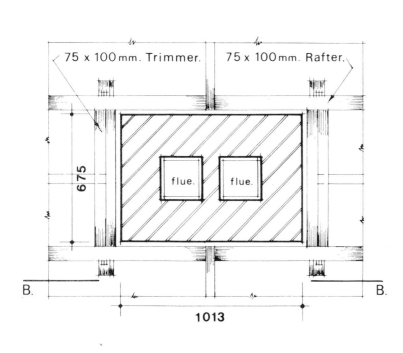

75 x 100mm. Trimmer.   75 x 100mm. Rafter.

675

flue. flue.

B. B.

1013

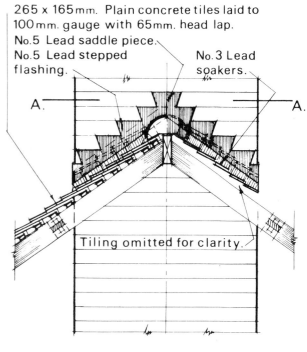

265 x 165mm. Plain concrete tiles laid to 100mm. gauge with 65mm. head lap.
No.5 Lead saddle piece.
No.5 Lead stepped flashing.

No.3 Lead soakers.

A. A.

Tiling omitted for clarity.

PLAN OF CHIMNEY AT A.A.

SECTION THROUGH ROOF AT B.B.

Scale.   1 : 20. .

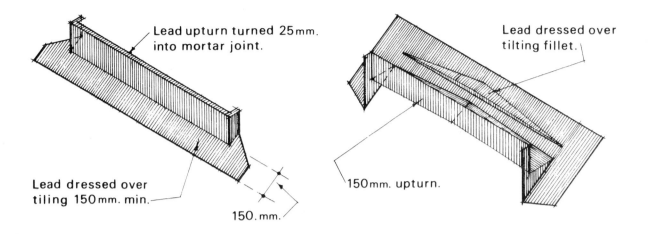

Lead upturn turned 25mm. into mortar joint.

Lead dressed over tiling fillet.

150mm. upturn.

Lead dressed over tiling 150mm. min.

150. mm.

APRON FLASHING.

BACK GUTTER WITH FLAT SOLE.

No.5 Lead flashing stepped to follow brickwork coursing and dressed over upstands to soakers.

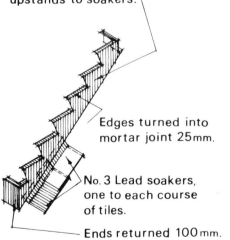

Edges turned into mortar joint 25mm.

No. 3 Lead soakers, one to each course of tiles.

Ends returned 100mm.

STEPPED FLASHING.

No.5 Lead saddle dressed over lead soakers to tile ridge course, turned up face of brickwork cloaking stepped side flashing and turned 25mm. into mortar joint.

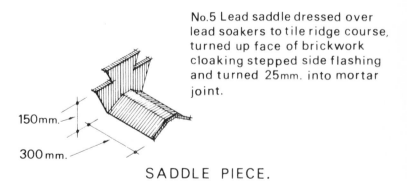

150mm.

300mm.

SADDLE PIECE.

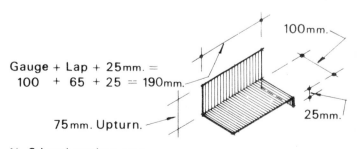

100mm.

Gauge + Lap + 25mm. = 100 + 65 + 25 = 190mm.

25mm.

75mm. Upturn.

No.3 Lead soaker, one to each course of tiles.

LEAD SOAKER. Scale 1 : 10.

Plate 12
CONCRETE FLAT ROOF

S.M.M. RULES | SECTION A

F.3.4.5.6.9.12.13.15.
L.3.4.5.7.
M.48.49.50.
N.1.4.28.
R.1.3.4.5.6.7.8.9.10.
T.3.13.
V.1.2.3.4.10.

APPROACH:-

Construction – concrete roof
      formwork
      reinforcement
      concrete kerb
      formwork

Coverings – asphalt coverings roof
           kerb

Eaves &
rainwater
installation – fascia board
      rainwater gutter & fittings
      rainwater pipe & fittings

Adjustments – nil

The general sequence –
Construction, Coverings,
Eaves and rainwater
installation and Adjustments
is used for all roofs
irrespective of type.

(Construction

      2.500
²⁄0.225 0.450
²⁄0.100 0.200
   L = 3.150
      2.000
      0.450
      0.200
   W = 2.650

S.M.M. F3.4.5.6.

3.15	Reinf conc (1:2:4)
2.65	suspended slab
0.10	n.e. 100 mm thk

Particulars of materials given in
Preamble in preference to description

3.15	Tamped surface
2.65	treatment unset
	conc.

S.M.M. F9.

2.50	Formwork hoz.
2.00	soffit slab, the
	surface fin fair incl
	m.g. exposed faces of
	conc after removal of
	fwk (In No1 surface)

S.M.M. F13.15.
Measurement between walls

$$\begin{array}{r} 3\cdot150 \\ 2\cdot650 \\ 2/\overline{5\cdot800} \\ \overline{11\cdot600} \end{array}$$

11·60	Ditto edge of slab & horz soffit of proj eaves 200 mm gth incl 20 × 10 mm recess (In No 1 member)

$$L = 3\cdot150$$

$$\begin{array}{ll} \text{Conc} \\ \text{Cover } \%0.040 = & 0\cdot080 \\ & \overline{3\cdot070} \end{array}$$

$$\begin{array}{ll} W = & 2\cdot650 \\ & 0\cdot080 \\ & \overline{2\cdot570} \end{array}$$

3·07 2·57	Steel fabric reinf 100 × 200 mm mesh whg 10·84 kg/m² inc 150 mm side & end laps in susp slab

$$\begin{array}{ll} L = & 3\cdot150 \\ W\,\%2\cdot650 = & 5\cdot300 \\ & \overline{8\cdot450} \\ \text{Angles }\%0.100 & 0\cdot200 \\ & \overline{8\cdot250} \end{array}$$

8·25 0·10 0·10	Conc (1:2:4) kerb n.e. 0·03 m² sectional area

Particulars of materials given in Preamble in preference to description

8·25	S.M.M. F13.15. Formwork to kerb size 100 × 100 mm one side fin fair incl m.g. exposed faces of conc after removal of fwk (In No 1 member)

(Coverings

$$\frac{3.150}{\text{kerb } \%.100 \quad 0.200}$$
$$2.950$$
$$2.650$$
$$\text{kerb } \quad 0.100$$
$$2.550$$

FALL 1:80

$$\frac{2550}{80} = 32$$
$$+ \text{MIN} \quad 15$$
$$\text{MAX} \quad 47$$
$$\text{MIN} \quad 15$$
$$62$$
$$\text{Avg} \quad \underline{31} \text{ mm}$$

2.95			
2.55			

Ct & Sand (1:4) Extl floated bed avg 31 mm thk to falls on conc

&

20 mm Thk 2 coat mastic asphalt roofg (B.S. 988 Table 1. Col 2) finished wi white spar chippings bedd in bituminous adhesive, flat Coverings, incl felt underlay to B.S. 747 Type A H (i) on floated bed.

2.95			

Fair rounded edge asphalt.

&

milled lead Code No 5. B.S. 1178 flashing 210 mm gth wi lead clips & tacks & 100 mm intermediate laps & one welted edge plugged & scd to conc.

S.M.M. T3.13.

Screeded bed is required when asphalt is bonded to base.

Particulars of materials given in Preamble in preference to description.

S.M.M. L4.

S.M.M. L5.
Above fascia board

S.M.M. M48.49.50.
Above fascia board.

	kerb	0·100
	bed	0·044
		0·053
	asph	0·020
		0·033
	angle	0·028
	top	0·120
	Girth on face	0·181

3·15			20 mm Thk mastic Asphalt a.b. Coverings to kerb 181 mm gth on face incl intl angle fillet, indd arris & fair indd edge.

S.M.M. L7.

2			angles

		2·650
	kerb	0·100
		2·550
		0·100
	bed	0·015
		0·085
	angle	0·020
		0·065
	angle	0·028
	top	0·100
	MAX GIRTH =	0·213
	MIN GIRTH =	0·181
	2)	0·394
	Avg GIRTH	0·197

2/2·55			20 mm Thk asph to kerb a.b. avg. 197 mm gth ditto

S.M.M. L7.
Asphalt ends to kerb

2			Ends

113

3.15	20 × 120 mm Wrot Sw. chamf fascia board plugged & scrd to conc	S.M.M. N1.4.28.	
2	Ends	S.M.M. N1.	
3.15	K.P.S. ③ gen wood surfs n.e. 300 mm gth _Extl_	S.M.M. V1.2.3.4.	
	§		
	100 mm Dia extl medium qual C.I. half round eaves gutter wi socketted jts bolted tog in red lead paste fxed on & incl C.I. bkts scrd to Sw. incl jts in the running length	S.M.M. R1.3.4.5.6.7.8.	
3.15 0.31	Prepare, prime ③ C.I. eaves gutter _Extl_	S.M.M. V1.2.3.10 inside and out	
2	E.O. stop end eaves gutter	S.M.M. R7.	
1	E.O. outlet ditto wi nozzle for 75 mm dia pipe	S.M.M. R7.	

2·50		75 mm dia extl medium quality C.I. rainwater pipe wi ears cast on & socketted jts fxd to faced bkk wi galvd pipe nails + hardwood dist. pieces incl jts in the running length		S.M.M. R9.1. length assumed	
		§			
		Prepare, prime ③ C.I. pipe n.e. 300 mm gth $\underline{3 \times 12}$		S.M.M. V1.2.3.10.	
1		E. O. swanneck 150 mm proj		S.M.M. R10.	
		§ E.O. shoe.		S.M.M. R10.	

Plate 12
REINFORCED CONCRETE FLAT ROOF

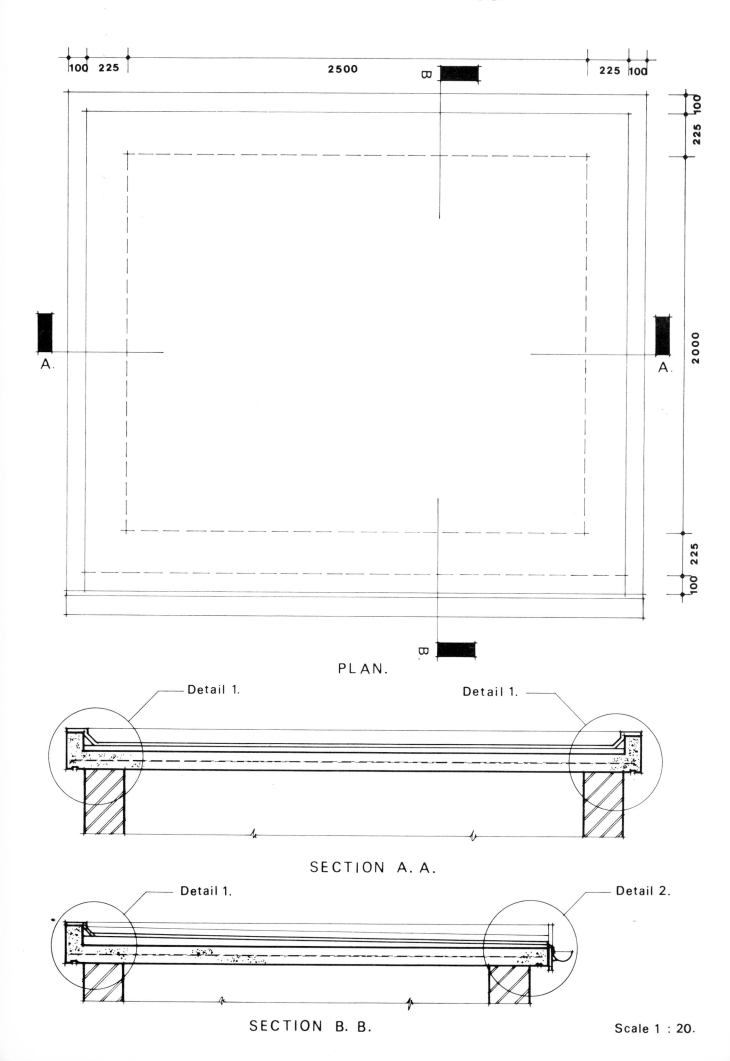

PLAN.

SECTION A. A.

SECTION B. B.

Scale 1 : 20.

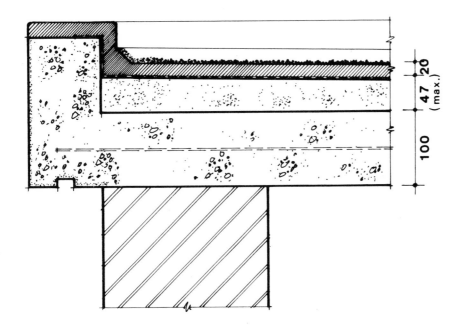

20
47 (max.)
100

CURB DETAIL 1.   Scale 1 : 5.

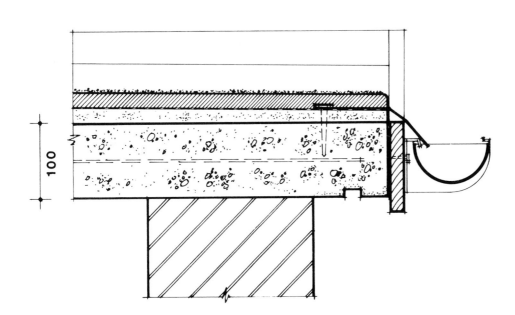

100

EAVES DETAIL 2.   Scale 1 : 5.

All insitu concrete.(1 : 2 : 4)
One layer fabric reinforcement 100 x 200mm. mesh weighing 10.840 kg/m²
with 150mm. laps.
Concrete soffit and exposed edge fair faced.
20mm. thick two coat mastic asphalte (B.S. 988 Table 1,col 2,) roof covering on felt
underlay to B.S. 747, Type A4 (i); finished with white spar chippings bedded in
bitumen adhesive; on cement and sand (1 : 4) screed (min. 15mm. thick to fall 1 : 80.)
Milled lead flashing Code 5 B.S. 1178. Medium quality cast-iron rainwater installation.
20 x 120mm. Softwood fascia painted two undercoats one coat gloss finish.

Plate 13
TIMBER FLAT ROOF

S.M.M. RULES:-	SECTION A			
	G43.			
	M1.3.4.33.34.36.			
	N1.2.4.6.			
	R1.3.4.5.6.7.8.9.10.			
	V1.2.3.4.			

APPROACH:-

Construction – plates
                        joists
                        firrings
                        boarding

Coverings   – flat roof
                        eaves

Eaves &
rainwater
installation – fascia board
                        rainwater gutter & fittings
                        rainwater pipe & fittings

Adjustments – nil

The sequence of measurement
follows closely the order of
construction

(Construction

2.200

Walls
2/0.275   0.550
              2.750

<u>S.M.M. N1.3.</u>
For measurement of labours, ends,
angles, mitres, intersections etc.

<u>S.M.M. N1.2.</u>
Particulars of quality given in
Preamble in preference to description.

2/2.75   75 × 50 mm Stawn   –   plate
Elev. flat roofs

&

Bed plate 75mm
wide in mor (1:1:6)

<u>S.M.M. G43.</u>
Brickwork assumed measured to
underside of plate

Intl 4.000
Clearance
2/0.025 = 0.050
& jsts
2/0.025 = 0.050 = 0.100
                        3.900

<u>3900</u> = 9 + 1 + 1 = 11
400

<u>S.M.M. N1.2.</u>
Particulars of quality given in
Preamble in preference to description

11/2.75   50 × 125 mm ditto   –   joists

		Joists = 2·750		S.M.M. N1.6.

Joists = 2·750
fall = 1:60

$$\frac{2750}{60} = 46 \text{ mm fall}$$
$$\frac{20}{66} \text{ MIN} \quad \text{MAX}$$
$$\frac{20}{86}$$
Avg = 43 mm

11 2/	2·75	50 mm wide sawn s.w. firrings avg 43 mm deep.

Particulars of quality given in Preamble in preference to description

		$\frac{1}{\text{nr}}$ 4·000
		walls 2/0·275 = 0·550
		4·550

S.M.M. N1.4.

	4·55	25 mm Thk
	2·75	s.w. butt jtd flat roof bdg to falls traversed for lead after laying

Particulars of quality given in Preamble in preference to description.

Coverings
Bdg 4·550
fascia
2/0·025 = 0·050
batten
2/0·025 = 0·050 : 0·100
4·650
2·750
0·100
2·850

S.M.M. M1.3.4.33.34.

	4·65	Three layer
	2·85	bitumen felt B.S. 747 flat roof covering of two layers asbestos based self finished bonding felt whg 18·1 kg/10 m² and one layer asbestos based mineral surf felt whg 36·2 kg/10 m² wi 75 mm laps, the first layer nailed to s.w. wi G.I. clout nails & subsequent layers continuously bonded in hot bitumen compound.

119

2/ 4.65	Turn down at eaves in mineral surface felt a.b. n.e. 150 mm gth incl welted drip nailed to dev. wi. G.I. clout nails	S.M.M. M36.
2/ 2.85		
	∮	
	25 x 50 mm wrot dev. batten	S.M.M. N11.
	(Eaves & R.w. (Installatᵗⁿ	
	Bkt o/a. 4.550 hilies ²/0.025= 0.050 ———— 4.600	S.M.M. N4. front fascia board.
4.60	25 x 210 mm wrot dev. t+g rebated fascia bd.	
2	hilies	S.M.M. N1.
	front fascia 0.210 fall 0.046 rear fascia 0.256	S.M.M. N4. rear fascia board
4.60	25 x 256 mm wrot dev. fascia bd a.b.	
2	hilies	S.M.M. N1.
	front 0.210 rear 0.256 2)0.466 Side Avg 0.233 2.750 ²/0.025 0.050 ———— 2.800	S.M.M. N4.5. side fascia boards

2/2·80	25 x 233 mm Avg fascia bd a.b. incl raking cuttg			
2/4·60	K.P.S. ③ general wood surfs n.e. 300 mm gth ExT	S.M.M. V1.2.3.4.		
2/2·80				
	Covering 4.650 Proj ²/0·025 = 0·050 4·700	S.M.M. R1.3.4.5.6.7.8.		
4·70	100 mm dia extl P.V.C. half round socketted eaves gutter jtd wi gutter straps & union clips fxd wi P.V.C. bkts scrd to sw. @ 900 mm ⁰/c incl jts in running length			
2	E.O. stop end	S.M.M. R7.		
1	E.O. outlet wi nozzle for 75 mm dia pipe	S.M.M. R7.		
3·00	75 mm dia extl P.V.C. rainwater pipe wi socketted jts fxd wi P.V.C. socket pipe clips wi extension bkts p.&s. to faced bkk @ 1000 mm ⁰/c incl jts in running length	S.M.M. R10. length assumed.		
1	E.O. shoe	S.M.M. R10.		

Plate 13
TIMBER FLAT ROOF

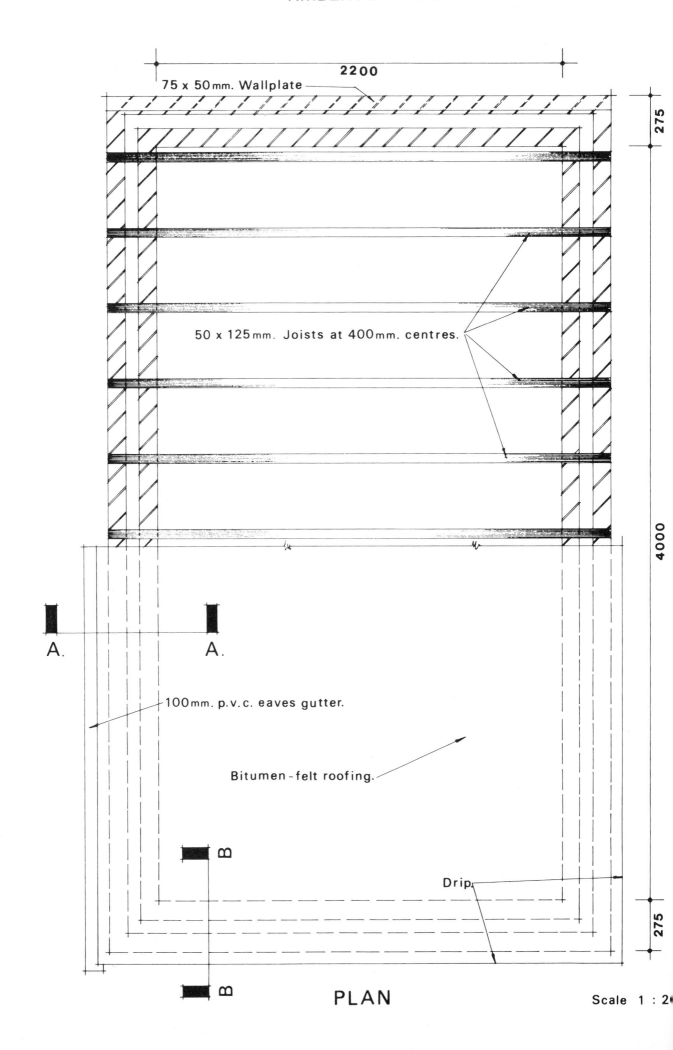

2200

75 x 50 mm. Wallplate

275

50 x 125 mm. Joists at 400 mm. centres.

4000

A.   A.

100 mm. p.v.c. eaves gutter.

Bitumen-felt roofing.

B

Drip.

B

275

PLAN

Scale 1 : 20

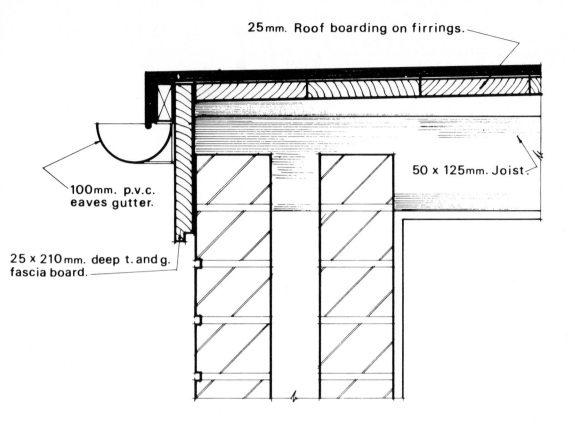

25mm. Roof boarding on firrings.

100mm. p.v.c. eaves gutter.

25 x 210mm. deep t. and g. fascia board.

50 x 125mm. Joist.

SECTION A.A.

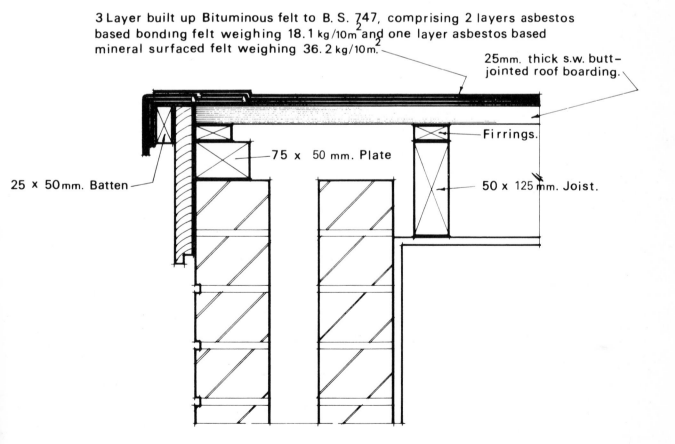

3 Layer built up Bituminous felt to B. S. 747, comprising 2 layers asbestos based bonding felt weighing 18.1 kg/10m² and one layer asbestos based mineral surfaced felt weighing 36.2 kg/10m².

25mm. thick s.w. butt-jointed roof boarding.

Firrings.

75 x 50 mm. Plate

25 x 50mm. Batten

50 x 125 mm. Joist.

SECTION B.B.

Scale 1 : 5.

Plate 14
TIMBER FLAT ROOF (Lead coverings)

S.M.M. RULES | SECTION A

G.47.52.
M.17.40.41.42.43.48.49.50.52.53.
N.1.2.3.4.5.6.9.
R.4.5.9.10.12.14.
V.1.10.

APPROACH:-

Construction – joists
firrings
boarding
drips
rolls
gutter

| The sequence of measurement follows closely the order of construction.

Coverings – flat roof
gutter
flashings

Rainwater
installation – rainwater pipe & fittings
painting

Adjustments – nil

_____

Construction

Ends
    2.400
2/0.100   0.200
      2.600
      4.300

S.M.M. N1.3.
For measurement of labours, ends, angles, mitres, intersections etc.

S.M.M. N1.2.

Wall
clearance 0.025
& joists
2/½/0.050 = 0.050   0.075

£ – £ =   4.225

$\frac{4225}{400}$ = 10 + 1 + 1 = 12 joists

Particulars of quality given in Preamble in preference to descript

12/2.60

50 × 200 mm
"Tanalised" sawn
sw. flat roofs

Preliminary treatment – tanalised.

124

$$\text{Length of fall} \quad \underline{4 \cdot 300}$$
$$\text{roof fall} \quad \overline{1 : 100}$$

$$\frac{4300}{100} = 43 \, mm$$

Add Drip $\underline{50}$

MAX fixing $93 \, mm$

MIN fixing $\underline{0}$

Avg $\underline{47 \, mm}$

2/ 2·40	50 mm wide sawn s.w. fixings avg 47 mm dp	Particulars of quality given in Preamble in preference to description

$$\text{lap at drip} \quad \begin{array}{r} 4 \cdot 300 \\ \underline{0 \cdot 065} \\ \overline{4 \cdot 365} \end{array}$$

S.M.M. N1.4.

4·37 2·40	25 mm thk s.w. butt jtd flat roof bdg to falls traversed for lead after laying	Particulars of quality given in Preamble in preference to description.
2·40	Rebate ditto & Chamfer ditto & 50 × 25 mm Wrot s.w. drip	S.M.M. N5. / S.M.M. N5. / S.M.M. N6.

DRIP

65 / 25 / 25

2/ 4·30	50 × 50 mm Wrot s.w. roll for lead	S.M.M. N1.9.
3	End ditto & Splayed end ditto	S.M.M. N1. / S.M.M. N1.

125

		lap at drip	2.400
			0.065
			2.465
		S.M.M. N1.4.	

2.44	25 mm thk sw. butt jtd gutter bdg 200 mm wide to falls, traversed for lead after laying	
0.20	Rebate ditto	S.M.M. N5.
	&	
	Chamfer ditto	S.M.M. N5.
2.40	50 x 50 mm sawn sw. bearer	S.M.M. N6.
	&	
	50 x 50 mm ditto plugged to like	S.M.M. N6.23.
1	50 x 25 mm wrot sw. drip n.e. 300 mm long incl ends	S.M.M. N6.
	(Coverings	
4.30	Underlay of waterproof building paper B.S. 1521 Class A, butt jtd & nailed to sw. wi G.I. clout nails	S.M.M. M17.
2.40		
0.20		
2.40		

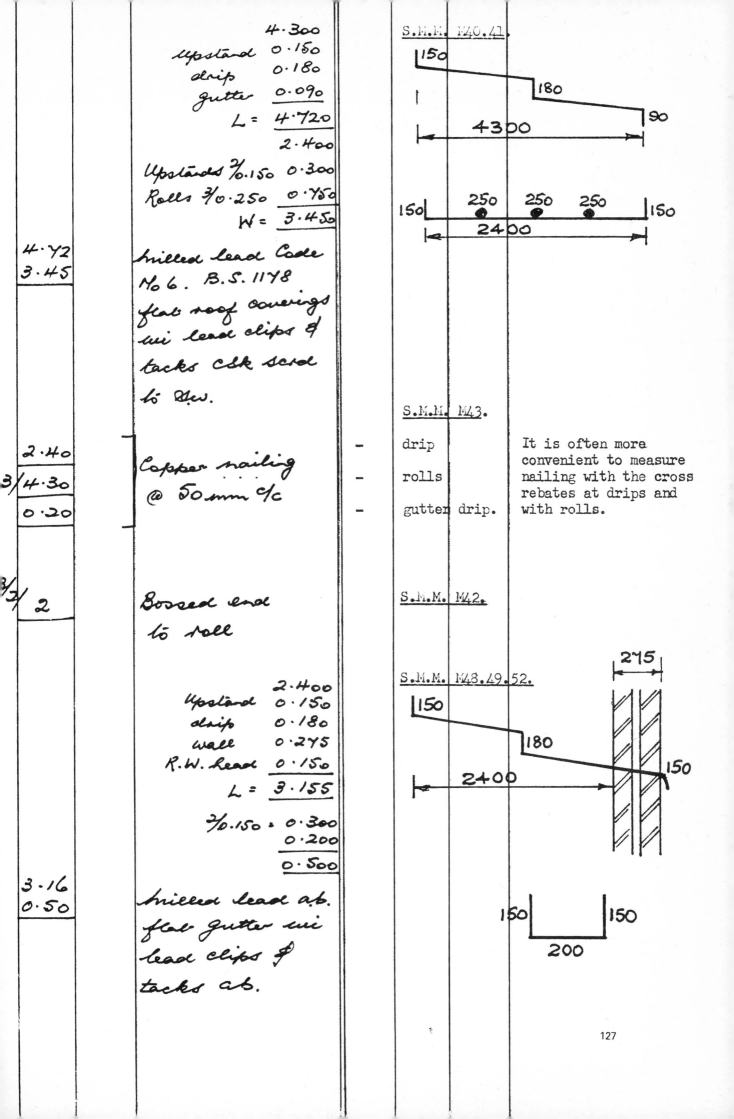

S.M.M. M40.41.

|150

|
4300 → 90

150 | 250 250 250 | 150
2400

		4.300
	Upstand	0.150
	drip	0.180
	gutter	0.090
	L =	4.720
		2.400
Upstands	⁷/0.150	0.300
Rolls	³/0.250	0.750
	W =	3.450

4.72	milled lead Code
3.45	No 6. B.S. 1178
	flat roof coverings
	wi lead clips &
	tacks csk scrd
	to dw.

S.M.M. M43.

– drip
– rolls
– gutter drip.

It is often more
convenient to measure
nailing with the cross
rebates at drips and
with rolls.

2.40	Copper nailing
3/4.30	@ 50mm c/c
0.20	

S.M.M. M42.

| 3/3/ 2 | Bossed end |
| | to roll |

S.M.M. M48.49.52.

|150

180

2400 →

275

150

		2.400
	Upstand	0.150
	drip	0.180
	wall	0.275
	R.W. head	0.150
	L =	3.155
	⁷/0.150 ·	0.300
		0.200
		0.500

3.16	milled lead a.b.
0.50	flat gutter wi
	lead clips &
	tacks a.b.

150 | 150
200

1		Dressing ditto thro' 200 × 150 mm opg in 275 mm wall and into R.W. head	S.M.M. M52.53.

&

Form opg size
200 × 150 mm
thro' 275 mm
thk hollow wall
seal all round
wi slates in mor
(1:1:6) & m.g.
c.b. & fegs.

S.M.M. G52.

	4·300
Gutter	0·200
	4·500
	2·400
2/	6·900
	13·800

S.M.M. M48.49.50.
Measure across opening to allow
for returns into each side of
opening.

13·80	Milled lead Code No 5. B.S. 1178 flashing 150 mm gth wi lead clips & tacks & 100 mm intermediate laps all lead wedged into groove.

&

Rake out hoz. jt
in bk̅k for
turned in edge
flashing & pt in
mor (1:1:6)

S.M.M. G47.

R.W.
(Installation

1	300 × 150 × 150 mm extl Rectangular pattern medium quality C.I. rainwater head wi ears cast on & nozzle for 75mm dia pipe fxd to faced blkk wi G.I. pipe nails & hardwood distance pieces	S.M.M. R4.5.14.
	&	
	Prepare, prime ③ ditto inside + out Ex72	S.M.M. V1.10.
3·00	75 mm dia extl medium quality C.I. rainwater pipe wi ears cast on & socketted jts fxd to faced blkk wi G.I. pipe nails & hardwood distance pieces incl jts in running length	S.M.M. R4.5.9.10. length assumed
	&	
	Prepare, prime ③ C.I. pipe n.e. 300 mm gth Ex72	S.M.M. V1.10.
1	bt jt C.I. R.W pipe to stoneware gulley	S.M.M. R12. Assumed gulley with vertical back inlet.

129

Plate 14
TIMBER FLAT ROOF (Lead coverings)

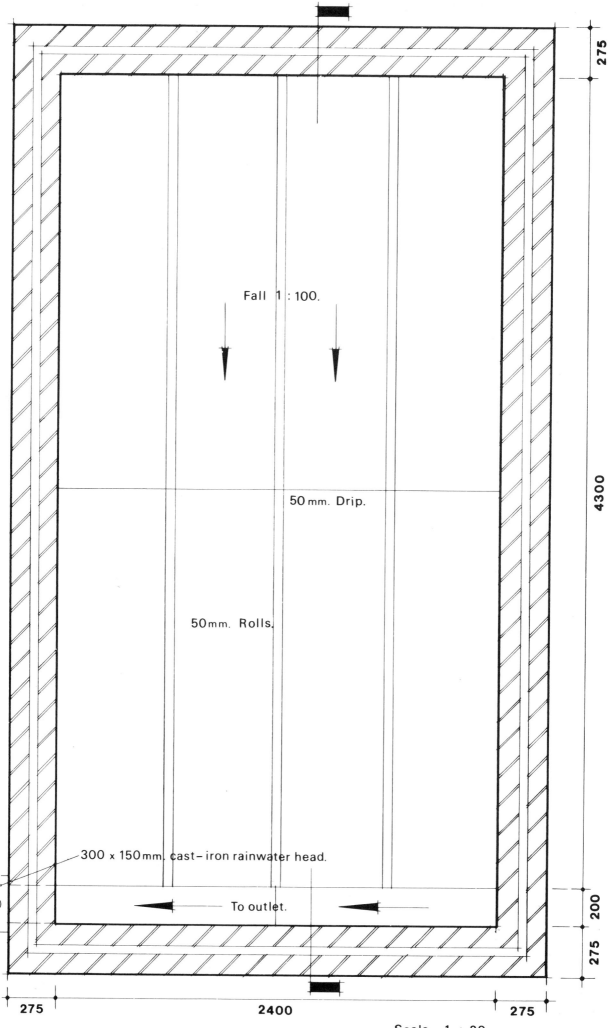

Fall 1 : 100.

50 mm. Drip.

50 mm. Rolls.

300 x 150 mm. cast–iron rainwater head.

To outlet.

275

275

4300

200

275

275

2400

275

Scale. 1 : 20

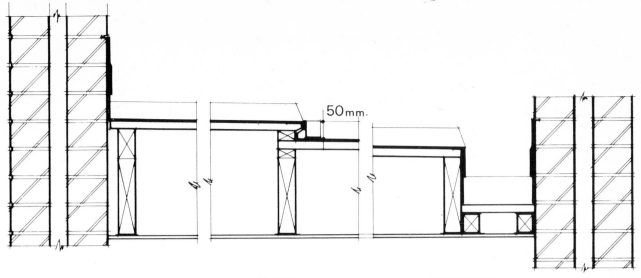

DRIP.   GUTTER.

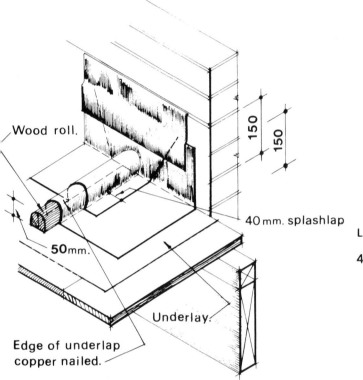

Timber rebated to take underlap copper nailed.

End of roll sloped back.

Wood roll.

150

150

40 mm. splashlap

50 mm.

Underlay.

Edge of underlap copper nailed.

WOOD ROLL WITH ABUTMENT TO WALL.

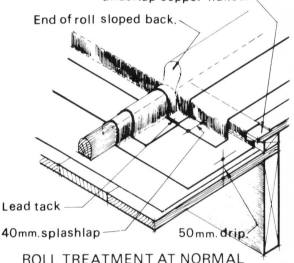

Lead tack

40 mm. splashlap 50 mm. drip.

ROLL TREATMENT AT NORMAL DRIP, ROLLS IN LINE.

50 x 200 mm. "Tanalised" softwood joists at 400 mm. $^{c}/c$.
50 mm. wide softwood firrings.
50 mm. softwood rolls, 50 mm. softwood drip with 50 mm. rise.
25 mm. thick sawn roof boarding.
Waterproof building paper underlay to B.S. 1521 Class 'A'.
Milled sheet lead roof coverings and gutter Code No 6 B.S. 1178.
Lead flashings B.S. Code No 5.
Cast iron rainwater installation painted two undercoats, one coat gloss finish.

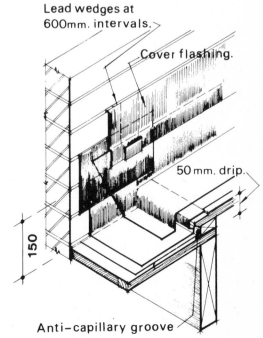

Lead wedges at 600 mm. intervals.

Cover flashing.

50 mm. drip.

150

Anti-capillary groove

SHALLOW DRIP WITH ABUTMENT TO WALL.

Chapter VI

Floors

Approach

(1)   Divide large buildings into sections of manageable size. Where a large project includes several buildings measure each as a separate unit.

(2)   Measure individual floors over all openings, recesses, projections and similar features which can be more easily dealt with by separate adjustment.

(3)   Sub-divide each floor, irrespective of type, into:

       (a)   Construction.
       (b)   Coverings.
       (c)   Adjustments for openings, etc.

(4)   Each building unit must be considered on its merits but a typical sequence of measurement would be:

GROUND FLOOR	Construction
	Coverings
	Adjustments
FIRST FLOOR	Construction
	Coverings
	Adjustments

(5)   The taker off must apply his knowledge of construction technology to determine the sequence of construction which in most cases will provide a logical sequence of measurement within the sub-sections listed above.

Measurement of floors

(1)   Concrete beds forming solid ground floors are usually measured in the structural group 'Foundations and work up to damp proof course'.

(2)   Timber ground floors are measured complete in this group including the sleeper walls, d.p.c., plates and air bricks.

(3)   Board or strip flooring which supports the load between the joists is measured with the floor and not with the internal finishings group.

(4)   Other floor finishings are more easily measured with the internal finishings group.

(5)   Maintain a constant floor level by adjusting the thickness of the bed to compensate for variation in the thickness of finishing materials.

(6)   Floor finishings in openings may be measured with the floor or with internal finishings but it is more consistent to measure these with the opening adjustment in the appropriate group.

(7)   Adjustments to form openings in floors for hearths, staircases, etc., are most conveniently made in the floors group while the taker off is still familiar with the floor construction and coverings.

(8)   Since skirtings form part of the wall finishings they are measured with the internal finishings group.

TIMBER FLOORS

Construction usually involves	plates and beams
	joists
	strutting
Coverings are either	boarding or flooring OR
	flexible sheet finishings

Calculation of joists required:

(1)   Find length of room between walls.

(2)   Deduct 25 mm clearance at each wall.

(3)   Deduct half of joist width at each wall to give the length, centre to centre, between first and last joists.

(4)   Divide by centre line spacing of joists to give number of spaces.

(5)   Add one to give number of joists required.

(6)   Should this calculation not produce an exact number of spaces decide either to increase slightly the spacing of joists or to add an extra joist. In most cases it is advisable to add an extra joist.

Strutting. This is rarely shown on drawings but must be measured where necessary.

TIMBER DOUBLE FLOORS

Construction usually involves   steel beams
plates
joists
strutting

Coverings are either   boarding or flooring OR
flexible sheet finishings

STEEL BEAMS. Unfabricated steelwork, such as that involved in most double floors, must be given under an appropriate heading for each different building or independent structure (SMM P3).

The unit of billing for structural steelwork is the tonne. Beams are measured linear and the weight per linear metre is indicated below the description of each member so that the worker up may calculate the total weight of the item.

TIMBER FRAMEWORK. Where a steel beam projects below the ceiling, any timber framework required to support the finishings to the sides and soffit of the steel beam is measured with the internal finishings group.

INSITU CONCRETE FLOORS

Construction usually involves   concrete
formwork
reinforcement
beams

Coverings include   boarding or flooring
insitu finishings
tile, slab or block finishings

The measurement of insitu concrete floors follows closely the sequence of measurement for insitu concrete flat roofs. Bending dimensions and the scheduling of bars for the reinforcement of concrete are detailed in Figures 38, 39, 40, 41 (Chapter V).

Plate 15
DETACHED HOUSE
(Timber first floor)

S.M.M. RULES   SECTION A

                  N1.2.3.4.5.7.

APPROACH:-   Construction – floor joists
                              herringbone strutting

            Coverings   – board flooring

            Adjustments – floor joists
                              herringbone strutting
                              board flooring

The sequence of measurement follows closely the order of construction.

(Construction

Room 1

               2·600
Ends 2/0·100 0·200
       L = 2·800
            7·200

     3·000
Ptn. 0·100   3·100
           4·100

Wall
2/0·025 = 0·050

℄ jsts
2/0·025 = 0·050 = 0·100
       ℄ – ℄ = 4·000

$\frac{4000}{400}$ = 10 Spaces
        + 1
        11 Joists

Room 2
     3·000
     1·800
     4·800

2/0·025 = 0·050
2/0·025 = 0·050 = 0·100
    ℄ – ℄ = 4·700

$\frac{4700}{400}$ = 11+1+1 = 13
        Joists

Room 3
     3·000
Ends 2/0·100 0·200
   L = 3·200

S.M.M. N1.2.3.
Calculate length and number of joists

– Mark this dimension on the drawing

– Joist length same as Room 1.

– Mark this dimension on the drawing.

4.500

$^2/0.025 = 0.050$

$^2/0.025 = 0.050 = 0.100$

$\pounds = \pounds = 4.400$

$\dfrac{4400}{400} = 11 + 1 = 12$ JOISTS

Room 4

7.200

Room 3 . 3.000

Ptn $= 0.100 = 3.100$

4.100

ends $^2/0.100$ 0.200

$L = 4.300$

12 JOISTS

1/ 2.80		
2/ 3.20	50 x 200 mm sawn s.w. floors	
2/ 4.30		
2/ 4.50	50 mm thk sawn s.w. h.b.s. 200 mm dp joists	
	(Coverings	
4.10 2.60	25 mm thk wrot s.w. t&g flooring wi splayed heading jts	
4.80 2.60		
4.50 3.00		
4.50 4.10		
	(Room 2 Stairwell Adjustment 1.200 end 0.100 1.300	
2.80	Ddt	
1/ 1.30	50 x 200 mm s.w. floors ab.	

Side notes:

– Mark this dimension on the drawing.

– Number of joists same as Room 3.

S.M.M. N1.2.
floor joists

Particulars of quality given in Preamble in preference to description

S.M.M. N1.2.
Strutting measured over the joists
i.e. wall to wall length.
Rooms 3 & 4 only.

S.M.M. N1.4.
Particulars of quality given in Preamble in preference to description.
Timber deemed to be fixed with nails – flooring brads not required in description.

– Trimming joist

– Trimmed joists

135

		2·850	
	end	0·100	
	joists	0·075	
	Dush 2/3 × 200 =	0·133	
		3·158	

2·80	Add	–	trimming joist
3·16	75 × 200 mm ditto	–	trimmer joist

S.M.M. N3.

1	Trimming 50 × 200 mm ditto and opg size 2850 × 1200 mm

Herringbone strutting not affected.

nosing 0·075		2·850
proj 0·035	0·040	
		2·890
		1·200
		0·040
		1·240

2·89	Ddt
1·24	25 mm Thk t + g floorg ab.

S.M.M. N5.7.

Ensure that nosings are not also measured with the staircase.

2·89	75 × 25 mm wrot. sw. nosing tongued to edge of floorg incl groove
1·24	

	Rm 4
	flue
Bkk	0·450
clearance	
2/0·025	0·050
	0·500

4·30	Ddt	–	trimming joist
0·50	50 × 200 mm sw floors ab	–	trimmed joist

		Bkk 0.450	
		Clearance 0.025	
		Jsts 0.045	
		Tusk 0.133	
		0.683	

4.30	Add		–	trimming joist
2/0.68	75 × 200 mm		–	trimmer joists
	ditto		

		Bkk 0.450	S.M.M. N3.
		Clearance 0.025	
		0.475	
		Ptn 0.100	
		0.375	

1	Trimming 50×200mm
	ditto arnd opg
	size 500× 375 mm

Harringbone strutting not affected.

		Bkk 0.450	S.M.M. N4.
		Blockwork 0.100	
		0.350	

Void not exceeding 0.50 square
metres but S.M.M. A3. deduction
at boundary.

0.45	Ddt
0.35	25 mm Thk
	t+g floorg ab.

S.M.M. N33.
Inserted by Worker-up.

Plate 15

DETACHED HOUSE (Timber first floor)

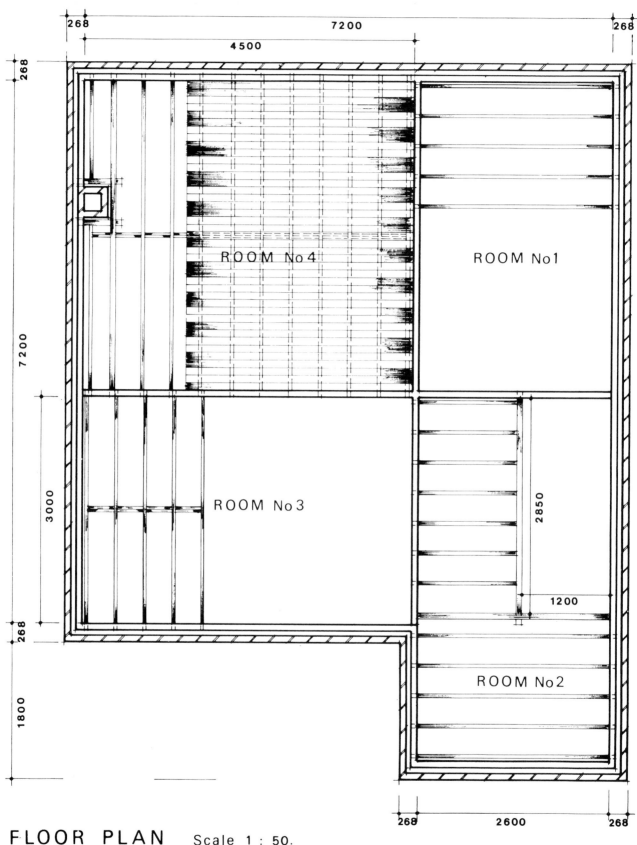

ROOM No 4

ROOM No 1

ROOM No 3

ROOM No 2

268 7200

4500

7200

3000

1800

268

268

2850

1200

268 2600 268

FLOOR PLAN   Scale 1 : 50.

50 x 200 mm. Softwood Floor Joists
75 x 200 mm. Trimmer and Trimming Joists.
50 mm Thick Herring Bone Strutting.
25 mm Thick Softwood T and G Board Flooring.
75 mm Softwood nosing to Stair Well.
100 mm Thick Block Partitions and inner skin.

DETAIL No 1

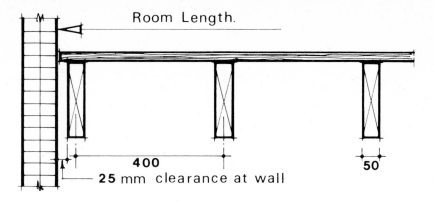

Room Length.

400

50

25 mm clearance at wall

NUMBER OF FLOOR JOISTS.

DETAIL No 2.

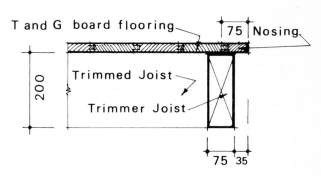

T and G board flooring

75 Nosing.

200

Trimmed Joist

Trimmer Joist

75 35

DETAIL No 3

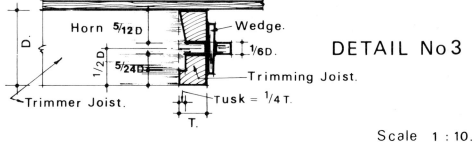

Horn $5/12$ D

Wedge.

$1/6$ D.

D

$1/2$ D

$5/24$ D

Trimming Joist.

Trimmer Joist.

Tusk = $1/4$ T.

T.

Scale 1 : 10.

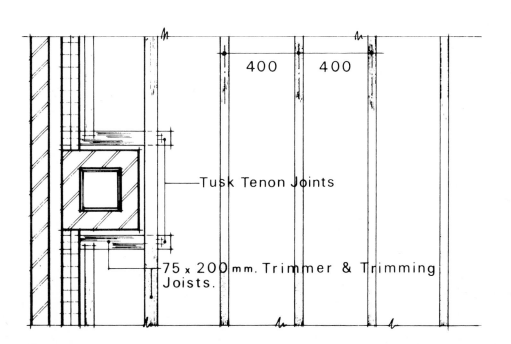

400 **400**

Tusk Tenon Joints

75 x 200 mm. Trimmer & Trimming Joists.

FRAMING TO FLUE. Scale 1 : 20

Plate 16
TIMBER DOUBLE FLOOR

S.M.M. RULES	SECTION A
	F.11.18.
	N.1.2.3.4.7.29.31.
	P.1.3.4.5.6.7.8.10.

APPROACH:-

Construction	- steel beam
	ends of beam
	plates
	bolts & holes
	floor joists
	herringbone strutting

Coverings	- strip flooring

Adjustments	- floor joists
	herringbone strutting
	strip flooring

The sequence of measurement follows closely the order of construction.

$$
\begin{aligned}
&\text{(Construction} \\
&\qquad\qquad 7.000 \\
&\text{ends } \tfrac{2}{0.150} \quad 0.300 \\
&\qquad L = 7.300
\end{aligned}
$$

S.M.M. P1.3.4.5.6.7.

UNFABRICATED STEELWORK :-

2/7.30

B.S. Beam size 305 × 152 × 80 kg/m 7300 mm long fixed at first floor level total weight =

tonne (In No 2 members).

× 80 kg =

S.M.M. P4.- Single members.
Structural function - beam
Position in the work - First Floor
Number required - two
Section type - B.S. Beam
Size - 305 X 152mm
Length - 7300mm
Total weight - Total length X 80kg

- Worker up to insert total weight

Item

Erect _____ tonnes
structural steelwork

S.M.M. P10.
- Worker up to insert total weight

2/ 2	Precast conc (1:2:4) padstone size 450 x 225 x 150 mm w/ keyed surface finish & b.i. to bkk in mor (1:1:6)	S.M.M. F13.	

S.M.M. N1.2.
Particulars of material given in Preamble in preference to description.

A continuous length is not essential since plate is bolted to steelwork.

2/ 2/ 7.00	75 x 100 mm sawn s.w. floors bolted to steelwork	

Plates
2/0.075 = 0.150
web   0.013
washers
2/0.003 = 0.006
nut   0.013
clearance 0.003
L = 0.185

$$\frac{7000}{750} = 9+1+1 = \underline{11\ BOLTS}$$

2/ 11	13 mm Dia m.s. bolt 185 mm long incl nut & washers	S.M.M. N31.

&

Hole 13 mm thk steel for 13 mm dia bolt

S.M.M. F8.
Holes for other trades

2/ 2/ 11	Hole 75 mm s.w. for ditto	S.M.M. N29.

141

Calculate length and number of jois[t]

$3/4.000 = 12.000$

ends $2/0.100 = \underline{0.200}$

$L = \underline{12.200}$ — Not continuous but in three separat[e] lengths.

7.000

wall

$2/0.025 = 0.050$

£ joists

$2/0.025 = \underline{0.050} = 0.100$

$\underline{6.900}$

$\dfrac{6900}{400} = 17+1+1 = \underline{19}$

$\underline{\text{JOISTS.}}$

19/12.20	50 × 225 mm ~~dawn~~ ~~sw~~ floors	— joists

2/2/19	notching & fitting end of timbers to metal	

3/7.00	50 mm Thk dawn Sw. L.b.s. 225 mm dp joists	

(Coverings

$3/4.000 = \underline{12.000}$

Particulars of quality given in Preamble in preference to descriptio[n]

12.00 7.00	25 mm Thk wrot Sw. t + g strip flooring wi splayed leading jts	

Timber deemed to be fixed with nails flooring brads not required in description.

142

(Stairwell
(adjustment)

$$3.500$$
end 0.100
JOISTS $L = \underline{3.600}$

$$4.000$$
end 0.100
TRIMMING JST $\underline{4.100}$

$$2.000$$
wall 0.025
& jsts
$^2/0.025$ $0.050 = \underline{0.075}$
$$\underline{1.925}$$

$$\frac{1925}{400} = 4+1+1 = \underline{6}$$
$= 5$ JOISTS
& 1 TRIMMER

	4.10	Dall	–	trimming joist.
5/	3.60	50×225 mm Clw.	–	trimmed joists.
		floors ab		

S.M.M. N1.2.

$$2.000$$
end 0.100
joists 0.075
Desk $\frac{2}{3} \times 225 = \underline{0.150}$
$L = \underline{2.325}$

	4.10	Add	–	trimming joist
	2.33	75×225 mm	–	trimmer joist
		ditto		

S.M.M. N3.

	1	Trimming	
		50×225 mm	
		ditto and opg	
		size 3500×2000 mm	

	2.00	Dalt
		50 mm thk
		L.b.s. ab.

		0.075	3.500			
		0.035	0.040			
			3.540			
			2.000			
			0.040			
			2.040			

3.54
2.04

Ddt.

25 mm Thk
t & g strip floorg

S.M.M. N7.

3.54
2.04

75 × 25 mm Wrot
S.w. nosing
tongued to edge
of floorg incl
groove.

Ensure that nosings are not also
measured with the staircase.

(Chy
(Breast
4.000
end   0.100
TRIMMING L= 4.100

0.450
clearance 0.025
end   0.100
TRIMMED = 0.545
1.350
clearance
2/0.025 = 0.050
& joists
2/0.025 = 0.050
1.450

$$\frac{1450}{400} = 3+1+1 = 5$$
= 3 JOISTS +
2 TRIMMING
JOISTS

2/4.10
3/0.58

Ddt.
50 × 225 mm
S.w. floors ab

– trimming joists
– trimmed joists

				1·350
		Clearance		
		2/0·025	0·050	
		joists		
		2/0·075	0·150	
		links		
		2/⅔/0·225	0·300	
		TRIMMER:	1·850	

2/	4·10	Add	–	trimming joists
	1·85	75 × 225 mm	–	trimmer joist
		ditto		

		1·350
	clearance	
	2/0·025	0·050
		1·400
		0·450
		0·025
		0·475

S.M.M. N3.

	1	Trimming 50 × 225mm
		ditto arnd opg
		size 1400 × 475 mm

Herringbone strutting not affected.

	1·35	Ddt
	0·45	25 mm Thk
		t + g strip floorg
		a.b.

S.M.M. N33.
Inserted by Worker up.

Plate 16
TIMBER DOUBLE FLOOR

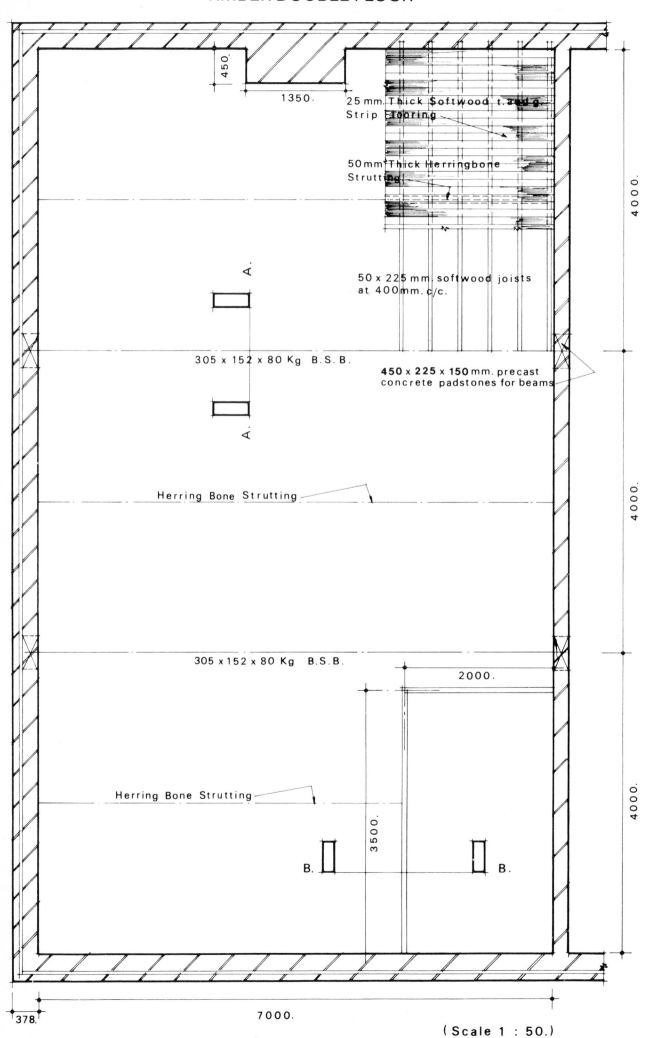

450.

1350.

25 mm. Thick Softwood t. and g. Strip Flooring

50mm. Thick Herringbone Strutting

50 x 225 mm. softwood joists at 400mm. c/c.

A.

305 x 152 x 80 Kg B.S.B.

450 x 225 x 150 mm. precast concrete padstones for beams

A.

Herring Bone Strutting

4000.

4000.

305 x 152 x 80 Kg B.S.B.

2000.

Herring Bone Strutting

3500.

4000.

B.

B.

378.

7000.

(Scale 1 : 50.)

DETAIL No 1.

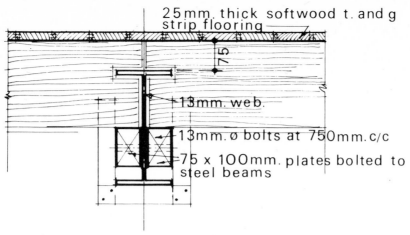

25mm. thick softwood t. and g
strip flooring

75

13mm. web.

13mm. ø bolts at 750mm. c/c

75 x 100mm. plates bolted to
steel beams

SECTION through beam at A. A.
Scale 1 : 10.

DETAIL No 2.

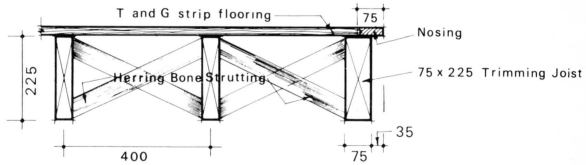

T and G strip flooring

75

Nosing

225

Herring Bone Strutting

75 x 225 Trimming Joist

35

400

75

SECTION through stairwell at B.B.
Scale 1 : 10.

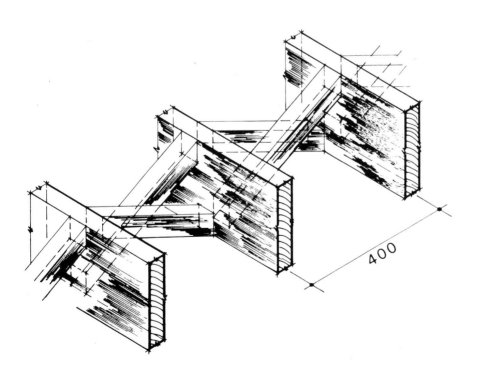

400

DETAILS OF Herring Bone Strutting.

Plate 17
REINFORCED CONCRETE
SUSPENDED FLOOR

<u>S.M.M. RULES</u>	SECTION A F.1.3.4.5.6.9.11.13.15.		

<u>APPROACH</u>:-	Construction - concrete floor
	                         formwork
	                         reinforcement
	                         concrete beam
	                         formwork
	                         reinforcement
			The general sequence,
			Construction, Coverings,
			Adjustments is used for all
			floors irrespective of type.

	Coverings - Internal finishings group		
	Adjustments - Nil		

	(Construction		<u>S.M.M. F3.4.5.6.</u>
	2/3.000 6.000		
	beam 0.300		
	L = <u>6.300</u>		
	W = <u>4.200</u>		
6.30 4.20 <u>0.15</u>	Reinf conc (1:2:4) suspended slab 100 — 150 mm thk		Particulars of materials given in Preamble in preference to description.
6.30 <u>4.20</u>	Tamped surface treatment unset conc		<u>S.M.M. F9.</u>
	floor 6.300 chase 2/0.100 <u>0.200</u> L = <u>6.100</u> 4.200 <u>0.200</u> <u>4.000</u>		<u>S.M.M. F13.15.</u> Measurement between walls.
6.10 <u>4.00</u>	Fwk hoz soffit slab (In No 2 surfaces)		For number of surfaces, refer to Practice Manual Page 19.

7/	6.25	12 mm dia straight m.s. bar reinf in susp slab.	—	S.M.M. F11. Schedule – Bar mark 1.

Dimension column entries:

- **7/ 6.25** — 12 mm dia straight m.s. bar reinf in susp slab. — S.M.M. F11. Schedule – Bar mark 1.

- **2d/ 4.15** — 6 mm dia ditto — Schedule – Bar mark 2.

- **7/ 2.30** — 10 mm dia ditto — Schedule – Bar mark 3.

- **6/ 4.15** — 6 mm dia ditto — Schedule – Bar mark 4.
  S.M.M. G11.
  Horizontal rough chase deemed to be included with the brickwork.
  S.M.M. F3.4.5.6.

- 4.20 / 0.30 / 0.30 — (Beam Reinf conc (1:2:4) susp slab 100–150 mm thk

- 4.20 — Fwk hor attached beam size 300 x 300 mm (In No 1 member). — S.M.M. F13.15.

- 4.00 / 0.30 — Ddt. Fwk hor soff slab — Formwork to soffit displaced by beam.

- **3/ 4.60** — 25 mm dia straight m.s. bar ab. — S.M.M. F11. Schedule – Bar mark 5 & 6.

- **14/ 1.38** — 6 mm dia m.s. bar reinf in stirrups in susp slab — Schedule – Bar mark 7.

Plate 17
REINFORCED CONCRETE SUSPENDED FLOOR

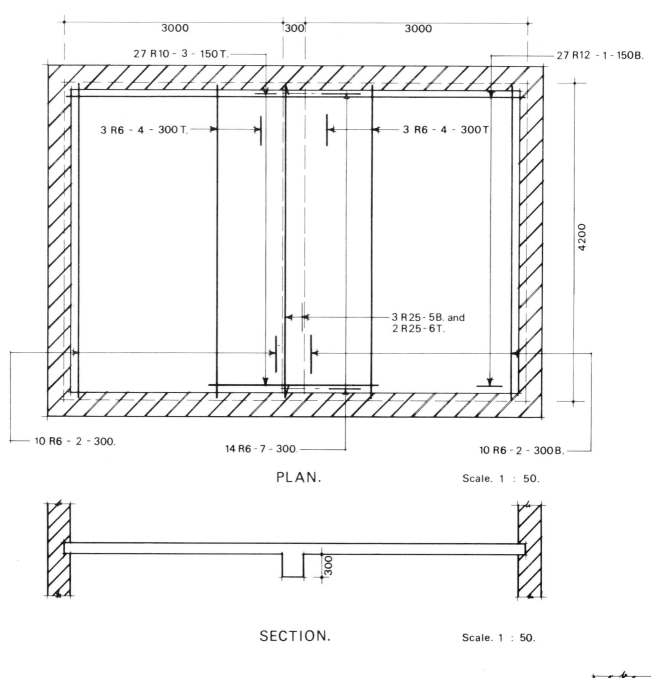

3000 300 3000

27 R10 - 3 - 150 T.

27 R12 - 1 - 150 B.

3 R6 - 4 - 300 T.

3 R6 - 4 - 300 T

4200

3 R25 - 5B. and
2 R25 - 6T.

10 R6 - 2 - 300.

14 R6 - 7 - 300.

10 R6 - 2 - 300 B.

PLAN. Scale. 1 : 50.

300

SECTION. Scale. 1 : 50.

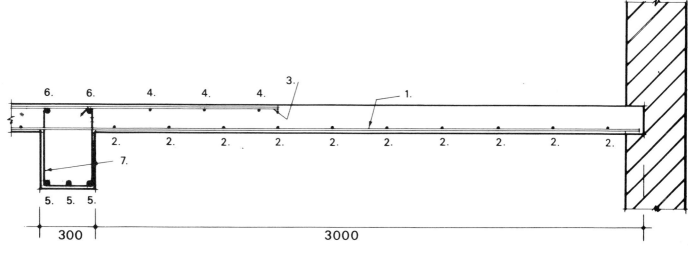

6. 6. 4. 4. 4. 3. 1.

2. 2. 2. 2. 2. 2. 2. 2. 2. 2.

7.

5. 5. 5.

300 3000

PART SECTION. Scale. 1 : 50.

Site Ref: Games Block, Shelton.

Member.	Bar mark.	Type & size.	No of mbrs.	No. in each	Total No.	Length of each bar † mm.	Shape Code	A* mm.	B* mm.	C* mm.	D* mm.	E/r mm.
FLOOR.	1	R12	1	2Y	2Y	6250	20	6250				
	2	R6	1	20	20	4150	20	4150				
	3	R10	1	2Y	2Y	2300	20	2300				
	4	R6	1	6	6	4150	20	4150				
BEAM.	5	R25	1	3	3	4600	33	4150				
	6	R25	1	2	2	4600	33	4150				
	7	R6	1	14	14	1375	60	390	240			

Bar type R — Round mild steel bars.

† Specified to the nearest 25mm.
* Specified to the nearest 5mm.

B.S. 4466 : 1969.
Code Shape.   20.

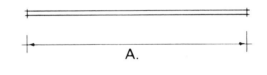

A.

Code Shape.   33.

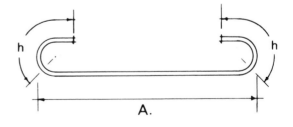

A.

Code Shape.   60

A.
B.

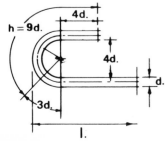

h = 9d.
4d.
4d.
d.
3d.
l.

Detail of semi- circular hook for use with shape code 33. showing minimum allowances.

Drawing References :-

27.   R 12. - 1.   - 150B.

Number of bars.   Reference No.

Mild steel 12mm.   150mm. centres in bottom
diameter.   of member or T in top of
                      member.

Chapter VII

Partitions

Approach

(1) Divide large buildings into sections of manageable size. Where a large project includes several buildings measure each as a separate unit.

(2) Examine each floor plan in turn and collect together in the waste the lengths of each type or thickness of partition. Thus only one dimension is usually required for each type or thickness of partition on each floor.

(3) Measure partitions over all openings, recesses, projections and similar features which can be more easily dealt with by separate adjustment.

Measurement of partitions

(1) Examination of the floor plan indicates that partitions appear to terminate at door openings but it must be remembered that they usually continue above the opening. The lengths of the partition on plan must therefore include door openings and adjustments should be made in the appropriate group. An exception to this principle occurs in the case of stud partitions and patent partitions, where openings are more easily adjusted when measuring the partition while the taker off is familiar with the construction involved. The finishings are usually adjusted with the doors group as before.

(2) Horizontal damp-proof courses may be necessary under partitions built upon a solid ground floor and if required are measured in this group.

(3) The height of block partitions is measured from the top of the structural floor and not from finished floor level.

Plate 18
BLOCK PARTITION

S.M.M. RULES	SECTION A.
	G.1.3.4.26.27.33.37.

APPROACH:- Measure partition over-all and adjust openings with the appropriate Group:-
Blockwork
Damp-proof course where required
Bonding ends of partitions.

The following in load-bearing superstructure –

S.M.M. G3.26.27.

	75mm	100mm
2/1.500 =	3.000	4.000
	3.200	0.100
	6.200	3.000
		0.100
		1.400
		1.500
		1.700
		3.000
		0.100
		3.000
2/3.200		6.400
		4.000
		2.500
		30.800

| 30.80 | 450 x 225 x 100mm thk lightweight conc. block partition w/ keyed surface fin b.s. b+j in mor (1:2:9). | Height of partition from structural floor. |
| 2.40 | | Particulars of quality given in Preambles in preference to description. |

| 6.20 | 450 x 225 x 75mm thk |
| 2.40 | ditto |

S.M.M. G37.

| 30.80 | One layer hessian based bit. felt hoz D.P.C. whg 3.8 kg/m² 100mm wide bedded in mor (1:2:9) no allowance made for laps. |

	6.20	Ditto 75 mm wide		S.M.M. G37.		
7/	2.40	Bonding ends 100 mm thk new blockwork to bkk incl forming pockets in new construction and extra material for bonding.		S.M.M. G33.		
3/	2.40	Bonding ends 75 mm thk ditto		S.M.M. G33.		

Plate 18
BLOCK PARTITION

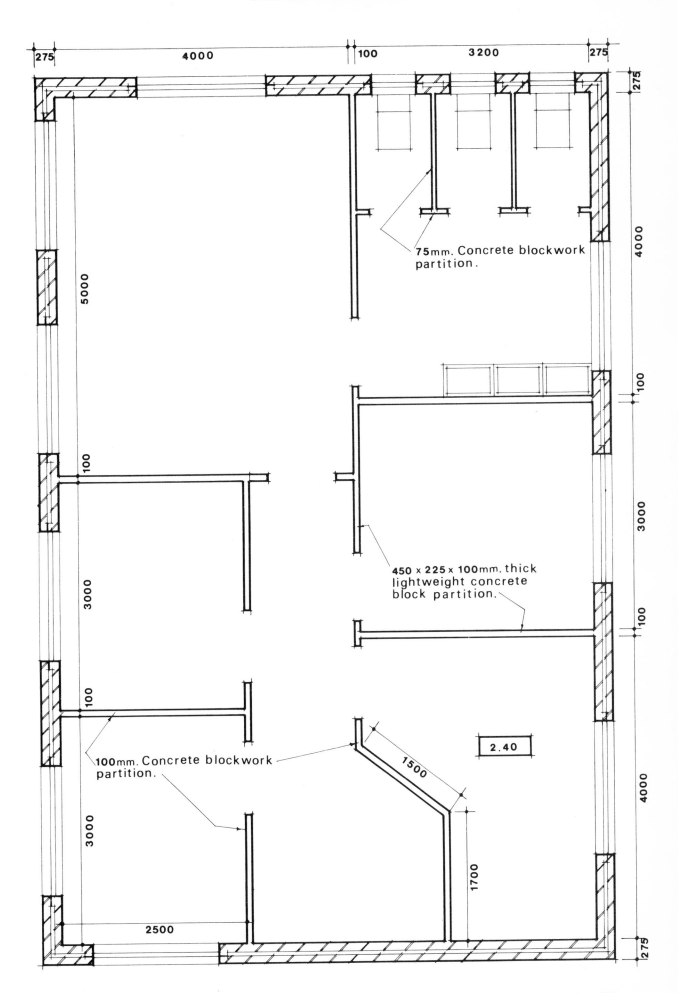

75mm. Concrete blockwork partition.

450 x **225** x **100**mm. thick lightweight concrete block partition.

100mm. Concrete blockwork partition.

275 4000 100 3200 275

275

4000

5000

100

100

3000

100

3000

100

3000

2500

1500

1700

2.40

275

Scale. 1 : 50.

Plate 19

STUD PARTITION

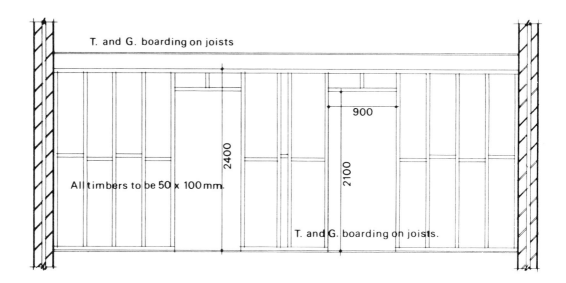

T. and G. boarding on joists

900

2400

2100

All timbers to be 50 x 100 mm.

T. and G. boarding on joists.

ELEVATION.

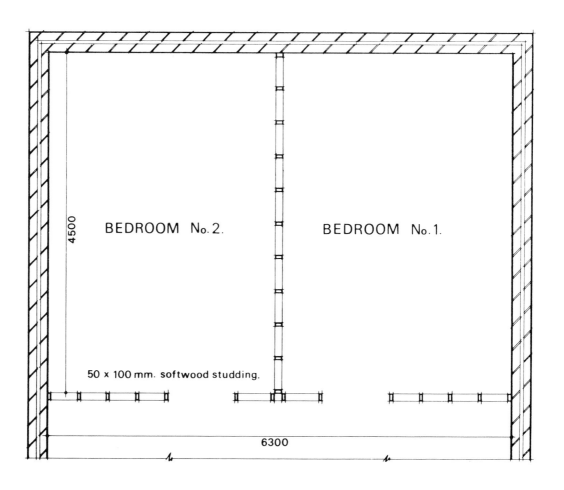

4500

BEDROOM No. 2.

BEDROOM No. 1.

50 x 100 mm. softwood studding.

6300

PLAN.

Scale. 1 : 50.

Plate 19
STUD PARTITION

S.M.M. RULES	SECTION A	
	N.1.2.3.28.	

APPROACH:-

Measure all carcassing timbers in partitions
including those forming openings:-
Carcassing timbers
Labours.

_____

	6·300	S.M.M. N1.2.3.
	4·500	
Head =	10·800	
Doors 2/0.900	1·800	
Plate =	9·000	
Studs		
25/0.050 =	1·250	
Noggings =	7·750	
	2·400	
2/0.050	0·100	
Studs =	2·300	
	2·400	
Head 0.050		
opg 2.100		
Door head 0.050 =	2·200	
	0·200	

10.80	50×100 mm sawn	–	Head
9.00		–.	Plate
7.75	sw. partitions	–	Noggings
14/11/ 2.30		–	Studs – counted from plan
2/0.20		–	Stud over door
2/0.90		–	Door head

3/2.30	Plugging bkk	S.M.M. N28.
	for softwood.	

Plate 20
PARAMOUNT DRY PARTITION (63.5 mm)

S.M.M. RULES

SECTION A.
        T.1.3.20.

APPROACH:-

Measure partitions over-all and adjust
openings with this Group:-
Partitions and openings
Fixings to head
        panels
        openings
        intersections
        ends of partitions
        skirting.

6·300	S.M.M. T1.3.20.
4·500	
10·800	

10·80
2·40

63·5 mm Thk
"Paramount" dry
partition, both
sides finished for
decoration jts filled
wi "Paramount"
jt filler lightly
rubbed down &
fxd to s.w. wi
galv. nails INTL

2/0·90
  2·10

Ddt ditto

Door openings.
S.M.M. T20 - No cutting - work
designed to use standard sheets
without cutting.

10·80

36 × 19 mm s.w.
head plate

S.M.M. T20.

head plate	2·400
	0·019
	2·381

6/
4/ 2·38

36 × 32 mm s.w.
intermediates
wedged into ptn

Panel - panel batten.

158

$$
\begin{array}{r}
2.381 \\
2.100 \\
\hline
0.281 \\
\hline
\end{array}
$$

| 2/2/ | 0.28 | 36 × 19 mm Sw framings to opgs | | Door head |

| | 2.38 | 36 × 19 mm Sw intersection . . . . . . | | |

$$\frac{2400}{400} = 6$$

| | 6 | 36 × 32 mm Sw. block 150 mm long swedged into ptn | | <u>S.M.M.</u> <u>N11.</u> Intersection |

| 3/ | 2.38 | 36 × 19 mm Sw. Abutments to other finishings plugged to bkk | | <u>S.M.M.</u> <u>T20.</u> Ends of partitions. |

| 2/ | 5 | 36 × 32 mm Sw block a.b. | | <u>S.M.M.</u> <u>N11.</u> Skirting. |

159

Plate 20
PARAMOUNT DRY PARTITION (63.5mm)

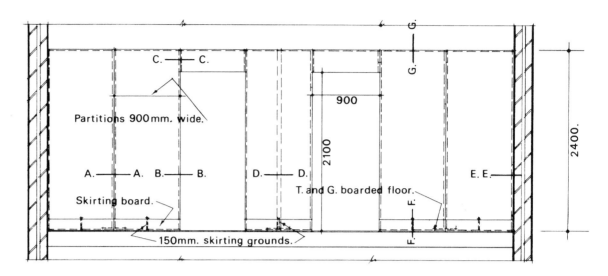

ELEVATION.

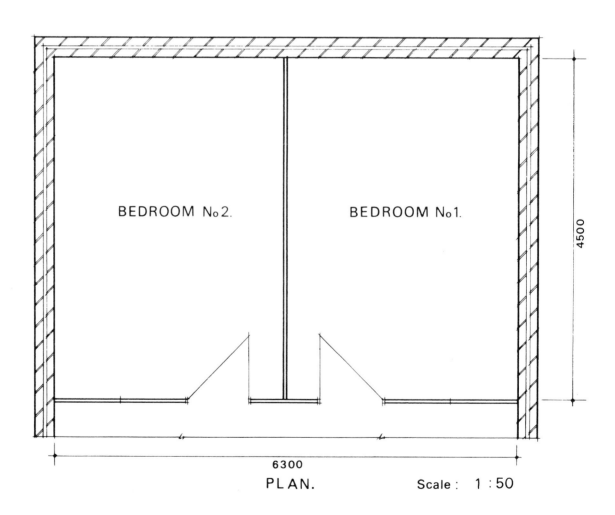

PLAN.   Scale :   1 : 50

Specification Notes.

Sawn softwood battens 32mm. for panel to panel joints and 19mm.
panel to solid joints, all 36mm. thick.
Panel joints filled with "PARAMOUNT" filler and rubbed down.

PANEL TO PANEL DETAIL AT A. A.

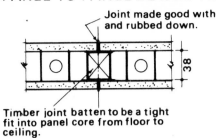

Joint made good with and rubbed down.

38

Timber joint batten to be a tight fit into panel core from floor to ceiling.

PANEL TO DOOR FRAME DETAIL AT B.B.

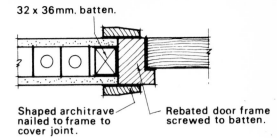

32 x 36mm. batten.

Shaped architrave nailed to frame to cover joint.

Rebated door frame screwed to batten.

DETAIL BETWEEN PANEL AND SPANDRIL PANEL OVER DOOR AT C.C.

Jointing batten to be a tight fit into 38mm. core x 19mm. thick nailed to the floor to ceiling batten.

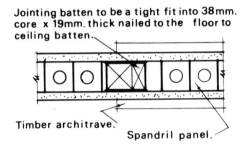

Timber architrave.

Spandril panel.

T JUNCTION DETAIL AT A POINT OFF THE JOINT BATTEN AT D. D.

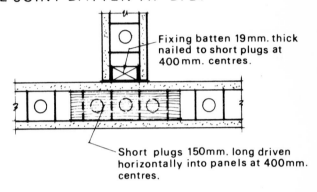

Fixing batten 19mm. thick nailed to short plugs at 400 mm. centres.

Short plugs 150mm. long driven horizontally into panels at 400mm. centres.

PANEL TO WALL DETAIL AT E.E.

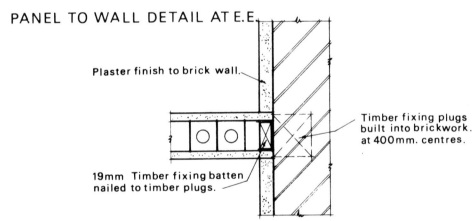

Plaster finish to brick wall.

Timber fixing plugs built into brickwork. at 400mm. centres.

19mm Timber fixing batten nailed to timber plugs.

BASE FIXING DETAIL AT F. F.

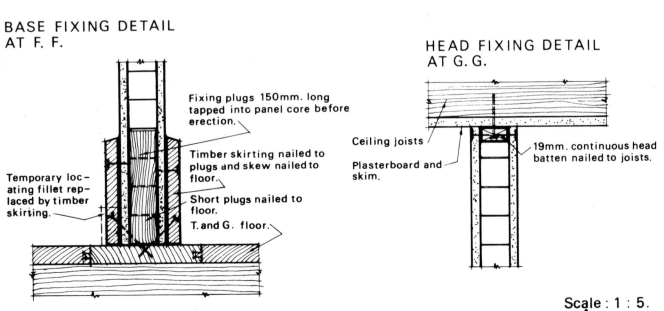

Fixing plugs 150mm. long tapped into panel core before erection.

Timber skirting nailed to plugs and skew nailed to floor.

Temporary loc-ating fillet rep-laced by timber skirting.

Short plugs nailed to floor.

T. and G. floor.

HEAD FIXING DETAIL AT G. G.

Ceiling joists

Plasterboard and skim.

19mm. continuous head batten nailed to joists.

Scale : 1 : 5.

Abbreviations in common use

a.b.	as before	clg.	ceiling
a.d.	as described	col.	column
addl.	additional	cos.	course
agg.	aggregate	cpd.	cupboard
a.f.	after fixing	conc.	concrete
ard.	around	csk.	countersunk
art.	artificial	ct.	cement
asb.	asbestos		
asph.	asphalt	d/d	delivered
avg.	average	ddt.	deduct
		d.h.	double hung
b & p.	bed & point	dia.	diameter
b.e.	both edges	dist.	distemper
b.f.	before fixing	d.p.c.	damp-proof course
b.i.	build in	d.p.m.	damp-proof membrane
b.m.	birdsmouth	d.p.	distance piece
b.n.	bull nosed	dp.	deep
b.s.	both sides		
bal.	baluster	e.m.l.	expanded metal lathing
bast.	basement	e.o.	extra over
bdd.	bedded	ea.	each
bdg.	boarding	exc.	excavate
bk.	brick	excn.	excavation
bkt.	bracket	extl.	external
bldg.	building	extg.	existing
brd.	board		
brrs.	bearers	f.a.i.	fresh air inlet
bwk. or bkk.	brickwork	f.c.	fair cutting
b.o.e.	brick on edge	f.f.	fair face
B.S.	British Standard	f & b.	framed and braced
B.S.C.	British Standard channel	f.l. & b.	framed ledged and braced
B.S.E.A.	British Standard equal angle	f.l.	floor level
B.S.T.	British Standard tee	fcgs.	facings
B.S.U.A.	British Standard unequal angle	fdns.	foundations
		fin.	finished
B.S.U.B.	British Standard universal beam	fr.	frame
		frd.	framed
		fwk.	formwork
B.M.A.	Bronze metal antique	ftd.	fitted
casmt.	casement		
c & f.	cut and fit	g.f.	ground floor
c & p.	cut and pin	g.i.	galvanised iron
c & s.	cups and screws	g.l.	ground level
c.b.	common bricks	g.m.	gunmetal
c.bwk.	common brickwork	galv.	galvanised
cc.	centres	grano.	granolithic
c.c.	curved cutting	gth.	girth
c.c.n.	close copper nailing		
C.E.	cleaning eye	h.m.	hand made
c.i.	cast iron	h.n. & w.	head nut and washer
clg.jst.	ceiling joist	hoz.	horizontal
c.jtd.	close jointed	h.b.s.	herring bone strutting
c.p.	chromium plated	h.b.w.	half brick wall
c.o.e.	curved on elevation	hdb.	hardboard
c.o.p.	curved on plan	h.c.	hardcore
c.s.g.	clear sheet glass	hdg.jt.	heading joint
c.t. & b.	cut tooth and bond	H.P.	high pressure
chfd.	chamfered	h.r.	half round
chy.	chimney	h.t.	hollow tile

162

ht.	height	R.C.	reinforced concrete
hwd.	hardwood	r.c.	raking cutting
h.w.	hollow wall	rdd.	rounded
inc.	including	reinf.	reinforced or reinforcement
intl.	internal	r.e.	rodding eye
inv.	invert	r.l.	reduced levels
i.c.	inspection chamber	r.l.jt.	red lead joint
		r.m.e.	returned mitred end
jap.	jappaned	r.o.j.	rake out joint
jst.	joist	r.s.c.	rolled steel channel
jt.	joint	r.s.j.	rolled steel joist
jtd.	jointed	r.w.h.	rainwater head
		r.w.p.	rainwater pipe
K.P.S.	knot, prime, stop	reb.	rebated
		retd.	returned
lab.	labour	ro.	rough
l & b.	ledged & braced		
l.p.	large pipe	s.a.a.	satin anodised aluminium
l & c.	level and compact	s.b.j.	soldered branch joint
		s.d.	screw down
matl.	material	s.c.	stop cock
m.g.	make good	segtl.	segmental
m.h.	manhole	s.e.	stopped end
m.s.	mild steel	s.g.	salt glazed
m.s.	measured separately	s.jt.	soldered joint
mis.	mitres	s.l.	short length
mo.	moulded	soff.	soffit
mort.	mortice	s.p.	small pipe
msd.	measured	s.q.	small quantities
		s.w.	stoneware
n.e.	not exceeding	sk.	sunk
No. or Nr.	number	sktg.	skirting
		sq.	square
o/a	overall	s & l.	spread and level
o.c.n.	open copper nailing	s & v.p.	soil and vent pipe
o.s.	one side	stg.	starting
opg.	opening	swd.	softwood
orgl.	original		
③	three oils	T	tee
		t & g.	tongued and grooved
pbd.	plasterboard	t & r.	treads and risers
p.c.	prime cost	t.c.	terra cotta
p & s.	plank and strut	t.p.	turning piece
plas.	plaster		
plasd.	plastered	v.o.	variation order
p.m.	purpose made	v.p.	vent pipe
p.o.	planted on		
pol.	polished	wi.	with
pr.	pair	w.g.	white glazed
prov.	provisional	w.i.	wrought iron
prep.	prepare	w.p.	waste pipe
pt.	point	wdw.	window
ptd.	pointed	wthd.	weathered
ptg.	pointing		
ptn.	partition	X grain	cross grain
P.V.A.	Polyvinyl Acetate	X tgd.	cross tongued
P.V.C.	Polyvinyl Chloride		
pvg.	paving	mm	millimetre
r & s.	render and set	m	metre
r.f. & s.	render float and set	m²	square metre
rad.	radius	m³	cubic metre
		kg.	kilogramme